TEACHER'S GUIDE
Activity Book

Science

PEARSON

Scott
Foresman

Editorial Offices: Glenview, Illinois • Parsippany, New Jersey • New York, New York
Sales Offices: Needham, Massachusetts • Duluth, Georgia • Glenview, Illinois
Coppell, Texas • Sacramento, California • Mesa, Arizona

www.sfsuccessnet.com

Series Authors

Dr. Timothy Cooney
Professor of Earth Science and
Science Education
University of Northern Iowa (UNI)
Cedar Falls, Iowa

Dr. Jim Cummins
Professor
Department of Curriculum, Teaching,
and Learning
The University of Toronto
Toronto, Canada

Dr. James Flood
Distinguished Professor of Literacy
and Language
School of Teacher Education
San Diego State University
San Diego, California

Barbara Kay Foots, M.Ed.
Science Education Consultant
Houston, Texas

Dr. M. Jenice Goldston
Associate Professor of Science
Education
Department of Elementary Education
Programs
University of Alabama
Tuscaloosa, Alabama

Dr. Shirley Gholston Key
Associate Professor of Science
Education
Instruction and Curriculum Leadership
Department College of Education
University of Memphis
Memphis, Tennessee

Dr. Diane Lapp
Distinguished Professor of Reading
and Language Arts in Teacher
Education
San Diego State University
San Diego, California

Sheryl A. Mercier
Classroom Teacher
Dunlap Elementary School
Dunlap, California

Dr. Karen L. Ostlund
UTeach, College of Natural Sciences
The University of Texas at Austin
Austin, Texas

Dr. Nancy Romance
Professor of Science Education
& Principal Investigator
NSF/IERI Science IDEAS Project
Charles E. Schmidt College
of Science
Florida Atlantic University
Boca Raton, Florida

Dr. William Tate
Chair and Professor of Education
and Applied Statistics
Department of Education
Washington University
St. Louis, Missouri

Dr. Kathryn C. Thornton
Professor
School of Engineering and
Applied Science
University of Virginia
Charlottesville, Virginia

Dr. Leon Ukens
Professor of Science Education
Department of Physics, Astronomy,
and Geosciences
Towson University
Towson, Maryland

Steve Weinberg
Consultant
Connecticut Center for
Advanced Technology
East Hartford, Connecticut

Consulting Author

Dr. Michael P. Klentschy
Superintendent
El Centro Elementary School District
El Centro, California

ISBN: 0-328-12617-9

Unit A
Life Science

Unit B
Earth Science

Unit C
Physical Science

Unit D
Space and Technology

Activity Book Overview

Just as scaffolding provides the structure and support needed to construct a building, Scaffolded Inquiry in Scott Foresman *Science* provides essential support as teachers and students construct the skills and knowledge needed to build science literacy. The monograph on pages 2–4 explains how Scaffolded Inquiry is developed in the Directed Inquiry, Guided Inquiry, and Full Inquiry activities in Scott Foresman *Science*. Another monograph on pages 5–6 explains how to teach safety in the science classroom.

The Activity Book provides recording sheets for the Directed Inquiry, Guided Inquiry, and Full Inquiry activities in Scott Foresman *Science* Student Edition as well as the supplemental Scott Foresman *Science* Activity Flip Chart. A reproduction of the Activity Flip Chart pages are provided so that students can see the activities at their desks as well as in the Science Center. In addition, Process Skill Activities are provided to help students learn about and practice using science process skills.

In this Activity Book Teacher's Guide, you will find answers for the activity recording sheets as well as support materials. Class Record Sheets with scoring rubrics are provided for all of the activities. The rubrics are also provided in Activity Rubric masters that can be photocopied so that students can evaluate what they accomplished in each activity. The rubrics provide criteria covering the procedure, the recording of data, the process skills used, and the conclusions reached. The same criteria appear on the Class Record Sheets, which include a 4-point scoring rubric.

Some of the activities in the Student Edition require Activity Masters, which are identified in the materials list. You will find these Activity Masters beginning on page 23 of this Activity Book Teacher's Guide. You will also find suggestions for planning a Science Fair and a Family Science Night at your school.

Science Safety

You need to be careful when doing science activities. This page includes safety tips to remember.

- Listen to your teacher's instructions.
- Read each activity carefully.
- Never taste or smell materials unless your teacher tells you to.
- Wear safety goggles when needed.
- Handle scissors and other equipment carefully.
- Keep your work place neat and clean.
- Clean up spills immediately.
- Tell your teacher immediately about accidents or if you see something that looks unsafe.
- Wash your hands well after each activity.

Practice Observing

To **observe** means to use any of your five senses to find out about objects or things that happen.

You can practice observing by seeing, tasting, smelling, listening to, or touching objects.

What to Do

1 Choose four objects in the classroom.

2 Write the names of the objects on the chart.

3 Use your senses to observe the objects. Write what you found out about each one.

Things I Observe	
Object	**How It Looks, Sounds, Smells, Feels**
a globe	It is round and smooth.

Explain Your Results

1. Write the name of an object you observed using more than one sense. Write the senses you used to observe that object.

_____

_____

_____

2. Which of your five senses did you use most often?

_____

Practice Communicating

To **communicate** means to share what you learn. You can use words, pictures, charts, diagrams, or graphs.

Talking with your partner is communicating. You can practice communicating by describing animals.

What to Do

1 Think of an animal.

2 Give clues to a partner. Tell how the animal moves and looks. Describe what it does.

3 Record each clue in the chart until your partner guesses the animal.

Animal	Clues
	It hunts. It has 4 legs and a tail. It is orange with black stripes.

Explain Your Results

1. How many clues did you give?

_____

2. Which clues helped your partner the most?
Why?

_____

_____

_____

Practice Estimating and Measuring

Estimate and measure means to tell what you think an object's measure is. Then you measure it and tell the amount or size.

You can practice by estimating and measuring the height of your desk.

Materials

metric ruler or meter stick

What to Do

1 Make an estimate. How many centimeters is it from the top to the bottom of your desk?

2 Write down your estimate.

3 Use a metric ruler or meter stick to measure the number of centimeters.

4 Write down the number of centimeters.

Explain Your Results

1. What was the difference between your estimate and your measurement?

_____

2. What helped you to make a good estimate?

_____

_____

_____

Practice Collecting Data

Recording what you observe and measure is **collecting data.** You can record data in a table, chart, graph, or diagram.

You can practice collecting data. Make a chart that shows your height and a partner's height.

Materials
metric tape measure
masking tape

What to Do
1 Tape a tape measure to a wall. Tape the "zero" end at the bottom of the wall. Tape the end with high numbers as high as it will go.

2 Stand next to the tape measure. Put your back to the wall.

3 Have your partner write your height in the chart.

4 Switch roles. Write your partner's height in the chart.

Name	Height

© Pearson Education, Inc

Explain Your Results

1. What would you do if you had the height of every student in the room? How would you change the chart?

_____

_____

2. How could you record the same data using words or pictures instead of a chart?

_____

_____

_____

Practice Classifying

You **classify** when you group objects by how they are alike.

You classify when you think about how some animals are alike. Practice classifying by sorting animal cards.

Materials

index cards

crayons

What to Do

❶ Take 9 cards and draw one animal on each card. Draw 3 kinds of fish, 3 four-legged mammals, and 3 types of birds on the cards.

❷ Mix up the cards and give them to a partner.

❸ Look at the cards your partner gave you. Classify the cards into 3 groups.

❹ Talk with your partner about how you sorted the cards.

Explain Your Results

1. How did you and your partner classify the animals on the cards?

_____

_____

2. Name ways that the animals in each group are alike.

_____

_____

_____

Practice Inferring

Infer means to draw conclusions from what you observe or know.

You infer when you look at a picture and get an idea about what is happening. Practice inferring as you talk about pictures with a partner. Use this information:

In many places, trees grow leaves and flowers in the spring. All summer the trees have green leaves. In fall the leaves turn yellow, orange, and red. Then the leaves fall off. The trees have no leaves in winter.

Materials

paper

crayons

What to Do

1 Choose a season. Draw a color picture of a tree in that season.

2 Show your picture to a partner. Have your partner infer the season. Look at the picture your partner drew. Infer the season in your partner's picture.

3 Talk with your partner about your pictures. Talk about how you inferred what season each picture showed.

4 Look at the pictures in the chart. Infer the seasons. Fill in the chart.

Picture	Season

Explain Your Results

1. What clues in the pictures helped you infer the seasons?

_____

_____

_____

2. What other things in nature besides trees can help you infer what season it is?

_____

_____

_____

Practice Predicting

Predicting is telling what you think might happen.

Practice predicting by telling what will happen when you mix two colors together.

Materials
red paint
yellow paint
blue paint
brushes or sticks
paper plate

What to Do

1 Read the chart. Predict the colors you will get.
2 Write the color names in the chart.
3 Then mix the colors.
4 What happened? What color did you make?
Write the colors in the chart.

Colors to Mix	Color I Predict	Color I Made
red + yellow =		
red + blue =		
blue + yellow =		

Explain Your Results

1. How many colors did you predict correctly?

_____

_____

2. What helped you to predict the colors you
would make?

_____

_____

Name _____

Practice Making and Using Models

Making a model is making something to show what it is like or how it works.

You can make and use models to show how animals are different. Practice by making and using models of a spider and an insect.

Materials
pictures
14 pipe cleaners
clay

What to Do

1 Look at the pictures of the spider and the insect.

2 Count the body parts and legs of each.

3 Use clay and pipe cleaners to make a model of each.

4 Use the models to show a partner how the spider and the insect are different.

Explain Your Results

1. How did you use the pictures to help you make your models?

_____

_____

2. How are your models of a spider and an insect different?

_____

_____

Practice Interpreting Data

To **interpret data** means to use information you collected to solve a problem or answer a question.

Reading and thinking about information on a chart is interpreting data.

You can practice interpreting information on a weather chart.

What to Do

1 Look at the information on the chart.

Weather This Week				
Monday	Tuesday	Wednesday	Thursday	Friday

2 Use the information to think about the weather.
Find the sunny days.
Find the cloudy days.
Find the day it rained.

Explain Your Results

1. Which days were sunny?

_____

2. What days were cloudy?

_____

3. Which day did it rain?

_____

Practice Making Hypotheses

To **make a hypothesis** means to make a statement you can test to solve a problem or answer a question.

You can practice making a hypothesis by answering this question: Does a wet towel dry faster in a sunny, warm place or a dark, cool place?

Materials

2 paper towels
water

What to Do

1 Do wet towels dry faster where it is sunny and warm or where it is dark and cool?

2 Wet each towel in a tray filled with water.

3 Put one wet towel somewhere sunny and warm. Put the other wet towel somewhere dark and cool.

4 Test your hypothesis. See which towel dries first.

Explain Your Results

1. What was your hypothesis?

_____

_____

_____

2. How did you test your hypothesis?

_____

_____

3. Was your hypothesis correct?

_____

Practice Controlling Variables

To **control variables** means to change one thing that may affect what happens. Keep everything else the same.

You can practice controlling variables by doing an experiment with water, cups, and objects of different sizes. You will experiment to see which object makes water rise the highest.

Materials

3 objects of different sizes
3 cups
water
ruler

What to Do

1 Take three cups that are the same size and shape.

2 Pour the same amount of water in each cup.

3 Find a small, a medium, and a large object that will fit in a cup. Write or draw them in the chart.

4 Put an object in each cup.

5 Measure how much the water rises. Finish filling in the chart.

Object	Water Level

Explain Your Results

1. What did you find out in your experiment?

_____

_____

2. What variable did you change?

_____

3. What did you keep the same?

_____

Practice Making Definitions

Making a definition means using what you know now to describe something or tell what it means.

Practice making definitions by describing seeds, soil, water, and sunlight.

Materials

seed

soil

water

pot

What to Do

❶ Plant your seed and water it. Put it in a sunny place.

❷ Make definitions by filling in this chart.

Things that help a plant grow	What is it like?	How does it help a plant grow?
seed		
soil		
water		
sunlight		

Explain Your Results

Write a definition for a seed, soil, water, and sunlight. Write how each helps a plant grow. Use your chart to help you.

1. What is a seed?

_____

_____

2. What is soil?

_____

_____

3. What is water?

_____

_____

4. What is sunlight?

_____

_____

Practice Investigating and Experimenting

To **investigate and experiment** means to plan and do things to test a hypothesis or solve a problem. Then form a conclusion.

You can practice investigating and experimenting by trying to answer the question, "Does sugar dissolve faster in warm or cold water?"

Materials

2 plastic cups
sugar
teaspoon

What to Do

1. Fill one cup with warm water.
2. Fill the other cup with cold water. Fill both cups with the same amount.
3. Add 1 teaspoon of sugar to each cup. Stir.
4. Observe what happens to the sugar in each cup.
5. Record your results in the chart. Describe what you observe.

Cup with Warm Water	Cup with Cold Water

Explain Your Results

1. What problem did you investigate in this experiment?

_____

_____

2. Describe what you did to solve the problem.

_____

_____

_____

3. What was your conclusion?

_____

_____

Explore Do plants need water?

❷ How did the celery change after one day in the jar?

_____

❸ What did you predict would happen when you put water in the jar?

_____

_____

❹ How did the celery change after one day? Why did the celery change?

_____

_____

_____

_____

Explain Your Results
Predict What will happen if you take the celery out of the water?

_____

_____

Notes for Home: Your child learned how plants need water by observing what happens when a wilted stalk of celery is placed in a jar of water.
Home Activity: Discuss what happens to plants when it does not rain for a long time. Then discuss what happens to the plants when it rains. How is this like the celery activity he or she completed?

Investigate Do plants need light?

4—**5** Fill in the chart. Draw pictures to show the plants each day.

	Sunlight	Dark
Day 1		
Day 2		
Day 3		
Day 4		
Day 5		

Name _____

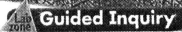
Explain Your Results

1. Which plant grew better?

_____

2. Infer What will happen if a plant does not
get light?

_____

_____

Go Further

What will happen if you move the plant from
the dark place to a sunny place? Try it and
find out.

_____

_____

Notes for Home: Your child learned how plants need sunlight to grow by
observing the effects of putting a plant in the sunlight for a week and putting a
plant in the dark for one week.
Home Activity: Try this planting activity at home. Plant pea or bean seeds in two
cups. Place one in the light and one in the dark. Observe the results.

© Pearson Education, Inc

Activity Book

Name _____

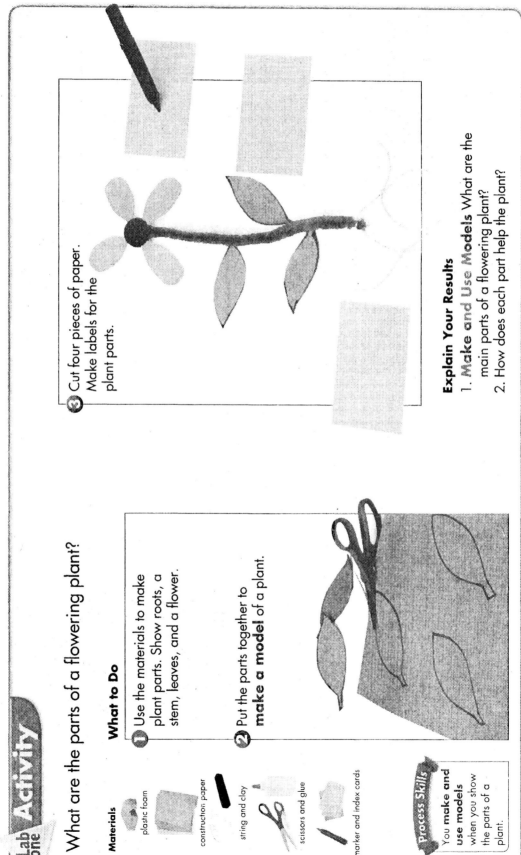

What are the parts of a flowering plant?

Materials

plastic foam

construction paper

string and clay

scissors and glue

marker and index cards

Process Skills

You **make and use models** when you show the parts of a plant.

What to Do

1. Use the materials to make plant parts. Show roots, a stem, leaves, and a flower.

2. Put the parts together to **make a model** of a plant.

3. Cut four pieces of paper. Make labels for the plant parts.

Explain Your Results

1. **Make and Use Models** What are the main parts of a flowering plant?

2. How does each part help the plant?

Use with Chapter 1

© Pearson Education, Inc

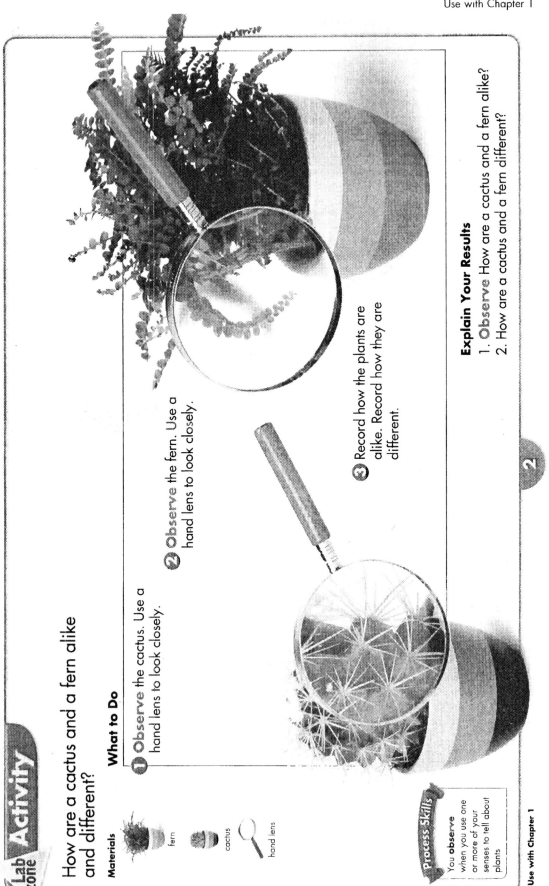

Activity

Lab zone

How are a cactus and a fern alike and different?

Materials

fern

cactus

hand lens

What to Do

① Observe the cactus. Use a hand lens to look closely.

② Observe the fern. Use a hand lens to look closely.

③ Record how the plants are alike. Record how they are different.

Explain Your Results

1. Observe How are a cactus and a fern alike?
2. How are a cactus and a fern different?

Process Skills

You **observe** when you use one or more of your senses to tell about plants

Use with Chapter 1

© Pearson Education, Inc

What are the parts of a flowering plant?

Explain Your Results

1. Make and Use Models: What are the main parts of a flowering plant?

_____

2. How does each part help the plant?

_____

_____

_____

_____

© Pearson Education, Inc

Notes for Home: Your child made a model of a flowering plant, labeled its parts, and communicated how each part helps the plant.
Home Activity: With your child, find a flowering plant. Discuss its parts and the function of each.

How are a cactus and a fern alike and different?

Explain Your Results

Observe In the chart below, record how the cactus and fern are alike and different.

	Alike	**Different**
Cactus		
Fern		

Notes for Home: Your child observed a cactus and a fern with a hand lens and communicated how the two plants are alike and different.
Home Activity: With your child, compare two types of plants and discuss how they are alike and different.

© Pearson Education, Inc

Name _____

Explore How are worms and snakes alike and different?

Explain Your Results
Feel the **models**. Tell about them.

_____

_____

Notes for Home: Your child made a model of a worm and snake and compared them.
Home Activity: Have your child try to name other animals that are like the worm and the snake.

Investigate How can an octopus use its arms?

❷ **Predict** how many suction cups you will need to open a jar.

_____

❸ Try to open the jar with suction cups. Make Xs on the drawing to show where you put them.

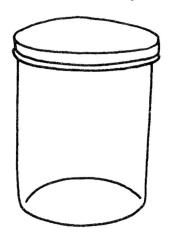

❹ How many suction cups did you predict? How many did you use? Color in the boxes on the graph to show your answer.

	How many suction cups will open a jar?							
Predict								
Test								
	1	2	3	4	5	6	7	8

Number of Suction Cups

Explain Your Results
Communicate Tell how you used the suction cups.

_____

_____

_____

Go Further
What other problems can you solve using suction cups? Try to solve the problems!

_____

_____

Notes for Home: Your child did an activity to find out how an octopus uses its arms.
Home Activity: Have your child try other small household tasks using suction cups.

Name _____

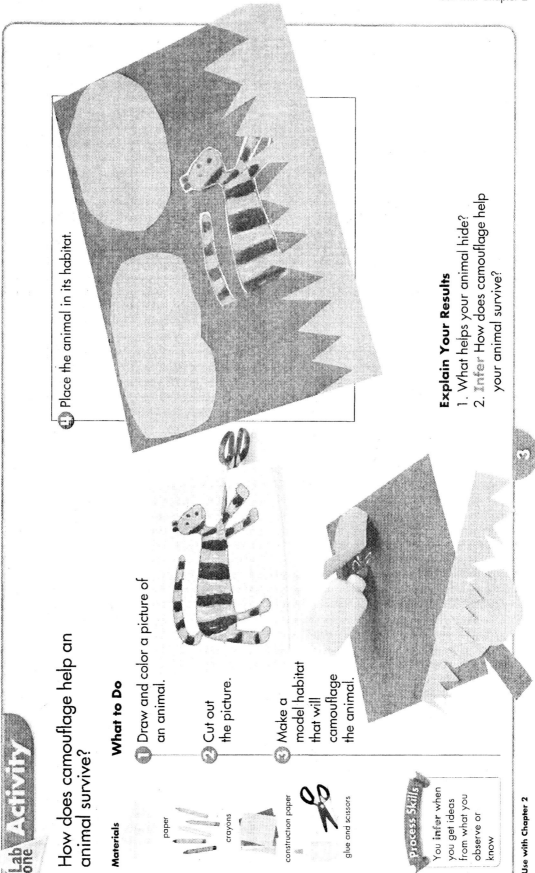

Lab zone Activity

How does camouflage help an animal survive?

Materials

paper

crayons

construction paper

glue and scissors

What to Do

1. Draw and color a picture of an animal.

2. Cut out the picture.

3. Make a model habitat that will camouflage the animal.

4. Place the animal in its habitat.

Explain Your Results

1. What helps your animal hide?
2. **Infer** How does camouflage help your animal survive?

Process Skills

You **infer** when you get ideas from what you observe or know

Use with Chapter 2

© Pearson Education, Inc

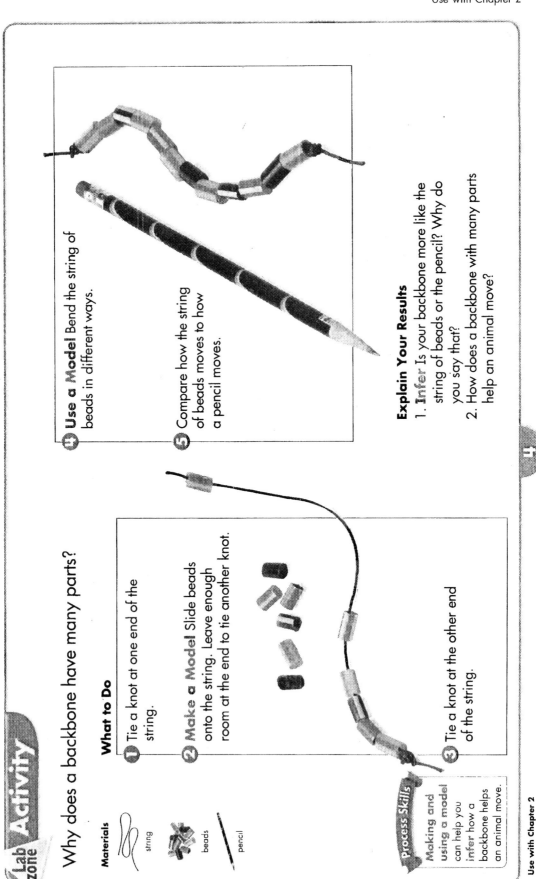

Why does a backbone have many parts?

Materials

string

beads

pencil

Process Skills

Making and using a model can help you infer how a backbone helps an animal move.

What to Do

1. Tie a knot at one end of the string.

2. **Make a Model** Slide beads onto the string. Leave enough room at the end to tie another knot.

3. Tie a knot at the other end of the string.

1. **Use a Model** Bend the string of beads in different ways.

2. Compare how the string of beads moves to how a pencil moves.

Explain Your Results

1. **Infer** Is your backbone more like the string of beads or the pencil? Why do you say that?

2. How does a backbone with many parts help an animal move?

© Pearson Education, Inc

How does camouflage help an animal survive?

Explain Your Results

1. What helps your animal hide?

_____

_____

2. Infer How does camouflage help your animal survive?

_____

_____

© Pearson Education, Inc

Notes for Home: Your child designed a habitat for an animal and inferred how camouflage helps an animal to survive in its habitat.
Home Activity: With your child, think of an animal that uses camouflage to help it survive. Discuss how the camouflage protects the animal in its habitat.

Why does a backbone have many parts?

Explain Your Results

1. **Infer** Is your backbone more like the string of beads or the pencil? Why do you say that?

_____

_____

2. How does a backbone with many parts help an animal move?

_____

_____

Notes for Home: Your child made a model of a backbone with string and beads and communicated how a backbone with many parts helps an animal move. **Home activity:** With your child, discuss the things a human's backbone allows him/her to do.

Name _____

Explore What does yeast need to grow?

3 **Estimate** How long did it take to see tiny bubbles in the cup?

_____

_____

Explain Your Results

What made the yeast change?

_____

_____

Notes for Home: Your child added sugar and water to yeast to observe that these living things need food and water. As yeast uses sugar as food, it produces carbon dioxide, a gas. The gas forms tiny bubbles in the water.

Home Activity: With your child, make a list of living things in and around your home that need food and water to live. List the types of food each needs. Include pets in your list.

Name _____

Investigate How can you model a food web?

4 Draw your food web. Write the names of all the living things.

My Food Web

Explain Your Results

1. Infer What do the web lines mean?

_____

_____

_____

2. How did you **model** a real food web?

_____

_____

_____

Go Further

How could you model a grassland food web?
Make a plan and try it.

_____

_____

_____

Notes for Home: Your child modeled a food web to understand how living things
depend on other livings things as a food source.
Home Activity: Take a walk around your house or look outside your window to
find plants and animals that need one another to survive.

What is a food chain?

Lab zone Activity

Materials

construction paper

crayons

scissors

What to Do

1. Draw pictures of a leaf, an insect, a small bird, and an owl. Cut out the pictures.

2. Draw and cut out three arrows.

3. Place your pictures and arrows to make a food chain. Show what eats the leaf. Show what eats the insect. Show what eats the small bird.

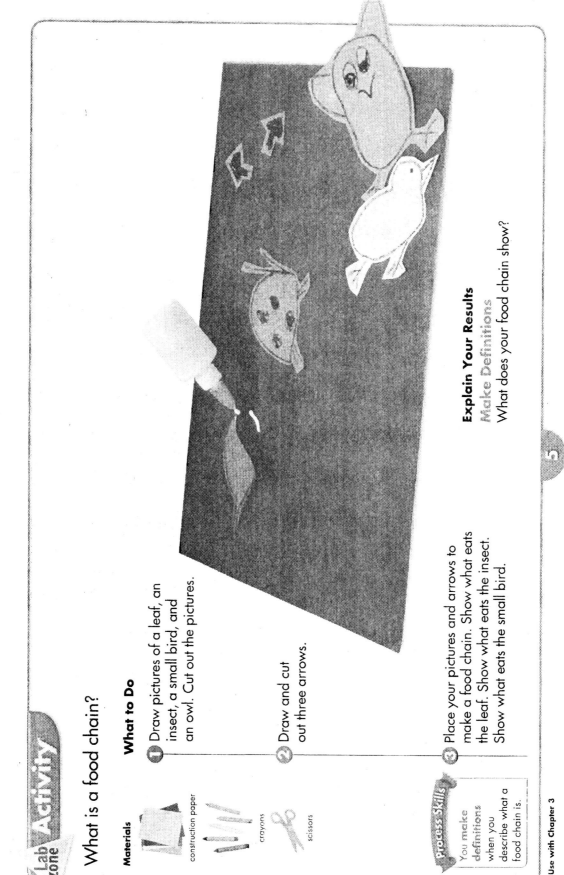

Process Skills

You make definitions when you describe what a food chain is.

Use with Chapter 3

Explain Your Results

Make Definitions
What does your food chain show?

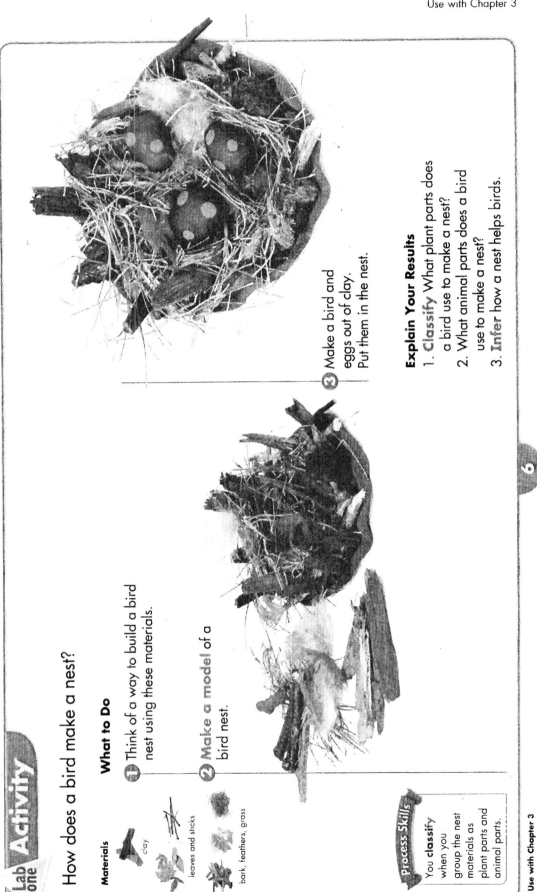

Lab zone Activity

How does a bird make a nest?

Materials

clay

leaves and sticks

bark, feathers, grass

What to Do

1. Think of a way to build a bird nest using these materials.

2. Make a model of a bird nest.

3. Make a bird and eggs out of clay. Put them in the nest.

Explain Your Results

1. **Classify** What plant parts does a bird use to make a nest?

2. What animal parts does a bird use to make a nest?

3. **Infer** how a nest helps birds.

Process Skills

You **classify** when you group the nest materials as plant parts and animal parts.

Use with Chapter 3

© Pearson Education, Inc

What is a food chain?

Explain Your Results
Make Definitions What does your food chain show?

_____

_____

_____

Notes for Home: Your child made a food chain using pictures of a leaf, an insect, a small bird, and an owl.
Home Activity: With your child, illustrate another food chain using crayons and drawing paper.

How does a bird make a nest?

In the box below, draw a picture of the bird nest you made.

```
┌─────────────────────────────────────────┐
│                                         │
│                                         │
│                                         │
│                                         │
│                                         │
│                                         │
│                                         │
└─────────────────────────────────────────┘
```

Explain Your Results

1. Classify What plant parts does a bird use to make a nest?

_____

_____

2. What animal parts does a bird use to make a nest?

_____

_____

3. Infer how a nest helps birds.

_____

_____

Notes for Home: Your child made a model of a bird nest and inferred how a nest helps birds.
Home Activity: With your child, discuss how nests help other animals and the things those animals use to build nests.

© Pearson Education, Inc

Name _____

Explore Which hand do different children use to write?

Explain Your Results

Infer What does the graph show?

_____

_____

_____

Notes for Home: Your child collected data that showed some children in the class are left-handed and others are right-handed. Your child learned one way in which people are different.

Home Activity: Observe differences in family members such as facial features, hair, or eye color.

Name _____

Investigate How does a caterpillar grow and change?

1 Use this chart to **collect data** on your caterpillars for 3 weeks.

	Observations
Week 1	
Monday	
Tuesday	
Wednesday	
Thursday	
Friday	
Week 2	
Monday	
Tuesday	
Wednesday	
Thursday	
Friday	
Week 3	
Monday	
Tuesday	
Wednesday	
Thursday	
Friday	

3 Predict what will happen next.

_____

_____

_____

Guided Inquiry

4 Draw pictures to show how the caterpillars changed.

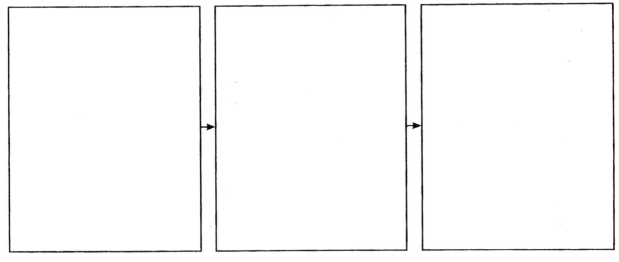

Explain Your Results

1. How did the caterpillars change?

_____

_____

2. Infer What happens inside of a chrysalis?

_____

_____

Go Further

Can you make a model of how a caterpillar grows and changes? Try it.

_____

_____

Notes for Home: Your child observed and recorded the stages of development of a Painted Lady butterfly.
Home Activity: You may wish to go to the library to read about other butterflies and moths that develop from a caterpillar, to a chrysalis, and then to an adult.

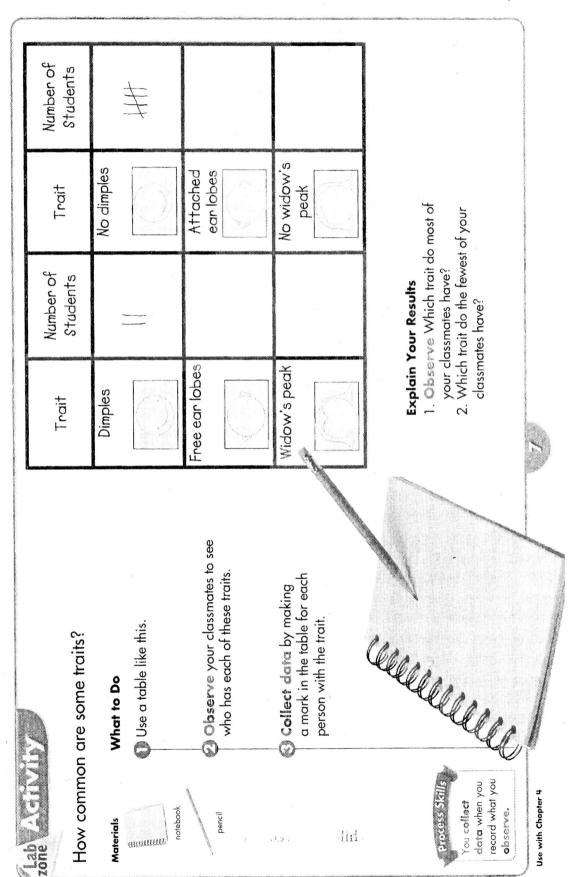

Lab Activity zone

How common are some traits?

Materials

notebook

pencil

What to Do

1. Use a table like this.

2. **Observe** your classmates to see who has each of these traits.

3. **Collect** data by making a mark in the table for each person with the trait.

Trait	Number of Students	Trait	Number of Students
Dimples	||	No dimples	⊬⊬
Free ear lobes		Attached ear lobes	
Widow's peak		No widow's peak	

Explain Your Results

1. **Observe** Which trait do most of your classmates have?

2. Which trait do the fewest of your classmates have?

Process Skills

You **collect** data when you record what you **observe**.

Use with Chapter 4

Lab zone Activity

What happens when a seed germinates?

Materials

radish seeds

paper towel

plastic sandwich bag

water

What to Do

1. Wet a paper towel. Squeeze out the extra water.

2. Fold the paper towel and put it in the plastic bag.

3. Place four radish seeds in the bag so you can see them. Seal the bag.

4. **Observe** the seeds every day for four days. Draw what you see.

Explain Your Results

1. Observe How do you know if the seeds germinated?

2. Predict Draw how the seeds would look after a week.

Process Skills

You think about what you observe in order to predict what will happen next.

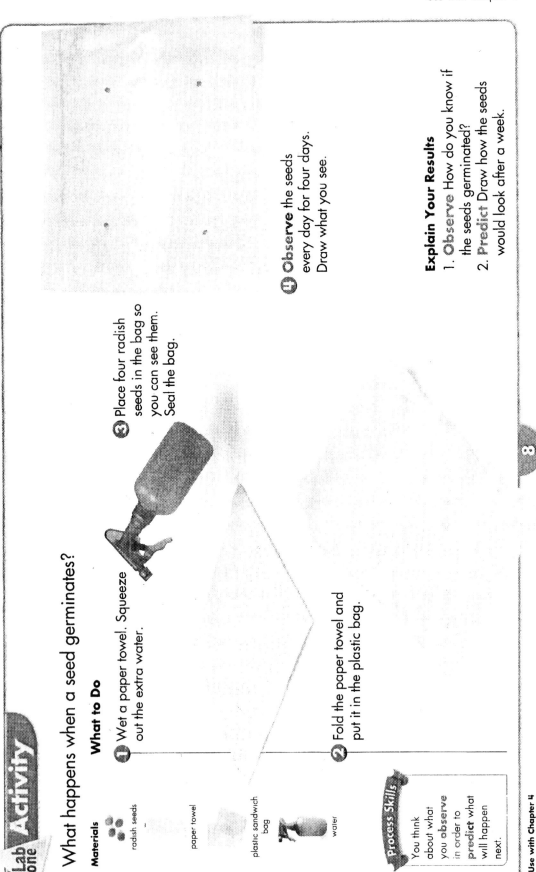

How common are some traits?

Fill in the chart below recording the number of students in your class with each trait.

Class Survey of Traits			
Trait	**Number of Students**	**Trait**	**Number of Students**
Dimples		No dimples	
Free ear lobes		Attached earlobes	
Widow's peak		No widow's peak	

Explain Your Results

1. Observe Which trait do most of your classmates have?

_____

2. Which trait do the fewest of your classmates have?

_____

Notes for Home: Your child observed his/her classmates and collected data about the number of traits his/her classmates shared.
Home Activity: With your child, discuss the traits members of your family share.

What happens when a seed germinates?

In the chart below, draw what you **observe** each day for four days.

Day 1	Day 2	Day 3	Day 4

Explain Your Results

1. **Observe** How do you know if the seeds germinated?

   _____

   _____

2. **Predict** In the box below, draw how you think the seeds would look after a week.

Notes for Home: Your child observed radish seeds germinate over a four-day period and predicted what the seeds would look like after a week.
Home Activity: With your child, plant seeds in a clear, plastic cup and observe the changes each day as the seeds germinate.

Name _____

Experiment Which bird beak can crush seeds?

Ask a question.
Which bird beak can crush seeds?

Make a hypothesis.

_____

_____

Plan a fair test.
Be sure to use the same kind of clothespins for models of birds' beaks.

Do your test.
Follow steps 1 through 3.

Collect and record data.

	Did the beak crush the seed? (Circle one for each beak.)
Heron's beak	
Cardinal's beak	

Name _____

Tell your conclusion.

Think about your test results. Do you think a heron or a cardinal uses its beak to crush seeds?

_____

Go Further

Which beak will pick up seeds faster? How can you find out?

_____

_____

_____

_____

Notes for Home: Your child used clothespins and craft sticks to make models of a heron's beak and a cardinal's beak. Then your child tested each to find out that a cardinal has a type of beak that is better for crushing seeds.

Home Activity: Look at photographs of birds in books and observe the beaks to decide what the bird eats. Check the text for explanations to see if your guesses were correct.

© Scott Foresman

Name _____

Explore How are soils different?

Explain Your Results

Observe How are the soils alike?

_____

_____

How are they different?

_____

_____

_____

_____

Notes for Home: Your child compared the odor, appearance, grain size, texture, and absorptive quality of potting soil and sandy soil.
Home Activity: Have your child examine soil in your backyard or in a park and then describe it.

Name _____

Investigate How do worms change the soil?

❹ **Collect Data** Draw what happens inside the bags.

Compost Bags		
	Bag With Worms	**Bag Without Worms**
Week 1		
Week 2		
Week 3		

Explain Your Results

1. Which bag had more leaves after 3 weeks?

_____

2. Infer What did the worms do with the leaves?

_____

_____

Go Further

What would happen if you use more worms?
Investigate to find out.

_____

_____

Notes for Home: Your child learned how worms help in composting. He or she learned that worms eat leaves and incorporate the waste matter into the soil. **Home Activity:** Have your child use what he or she learned to discuss this question: *What happens to leaves in a forest? If no one rakes them up, where do the leaves go?* (The leaves are composted, just as they were in this activity.)

Name _____

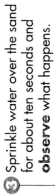

How does erosion affect land?

Materials

water

sand

pan

ruler

What to Do

1. Make a hill of sand on one side of the pan.

2. Use the ruler to measure the height of the hill.

3. Sprinkle water over the sand for about ten seconds and **observe** what happens.

4. **Estimate** the height of the hill after the water runs down it. Measure to check your estimate.

Explain Your Results

1. How did the height of the hill change after you sprinkled water on it?

2. **Infer** How does rain affect the land?

Process Skills

Estimating and measuring changes in the sand hill can help you **infer** how rain may affect land.

© Pearson Education, Inc

Activity Book

Activity

Lab zone

How can you reuse something?

Materials

empty plastic, cardboard, and metal containers

scissors and glue

craft materials for decoration

construction paper and markers

Process Skills

You **infer** how to reuse a container when you get ideas from what you **observe.**

What to Do

1 **Observe** the containers to see what they were used for.

2 **Infer** Think about how you could change one of the containers to use it in another way.

3 Make a drawing that shows how you could reuse the container.

4 Use the materials and your drawing to change one of the containers.

Explain Your Results

1. What does it mean to reuse something?

2. **Infer** Describe how you would reuse your container.

How does erosion affect land?

Record the data of the hill height below.

Height of Hill Before Erosion	Estimated Height of Hill After Erosion	Height of Hill After Erosion

Explain Your Results

1. How did the height of the hill change after you sprinkled water on it?

_____

_____

2. Infer How does rain affect the land?

_____

_____

Notes for Home: Your child experimented with sand to see the effects that rain has on land. They observed that rain causes erosion on land.
Home Activity: With your child, watch a rainstorm and observe erosion happening to the land.

How can you reuse something?

Draw a picture of your reused container in the box below.

（空白のボックス）

Explain Your Results

1. What does it mean to reuse something?

_____

_____

2. Infer Describe how you would reuse your container.

_____

_____

Notes for Home: Your child observed different containers and then changed one of the containers to use it in a different way. He or she learned about reusing objects.
Home Activity: With your child, choose another object from home that you would throw away and think of another use for it.

© Pearson Education, Inc

Name _____

Explore How much rain falls?

Explain Your Results

Infer How could you use this tool to measure how much rain falls?

_____

_____

_____

Notes for Home: Your child made a rain gauge from a plastic jar and then used the tool to measure the amount of rainfall.
Home Activity: Make a rain gauge at home. Use plastic food containers with a full-width mouth. Mark centimeters on masking tape along the side of the container.

Name _____

Investigate How can you measure weather changes?

❸ **Collect Data** Write how much rain fell each day. Write the temperature for each day.

Rain and Temperature for One Week		
Day of the Week	rain gauge (centimeters)	thermometer (°C)
Monday		
Tuesday		
Wednesday		
Thursday		
Friday		

© Pearson Education, Inc.

Explain Your Results

1. What does your chart tell you about the
weather for one week?
Classify each day as rainy or not rainy.
Monday _____
Tuesday _____
Wednesday _____
Thursday _____
Friday _____

2. Tell how the weather changed from day
to day.

_____

_____

_____

Go Further

How much rain do you think might fall in the
next 5 days? Measure to find out.

_____

_____

_____

 Notes for Home: Your child used a rain gauge and a thermometer to measure
rainfall and temperature for one week and recorded this information on a chart.
Then your child explained what the data on the chart told him or her about the
weather for the week.
Home Activity: Follow the daily weather reports on the news and record the
temperature or rainfall on a calendar for a few weeks or a month. Talk with your
child about the weather based on the data you collected.

© Pearson Education, Inc.

© Pearson Education, Inc

Lab zone ACTIVITY

What happens when cold air meets warm air?

Materials

2 jars

cold and warm water

red and blue food coloring

ice cubes

spoon

Process Skills

You **interpret data** when you explain what you **observed.**

What to Do

1. Half-fill a jar with warm water. Stir three drops of red food coloring into the water.

2. Fill the other jar $\frac{1}{4}$ full with cold water. Add ice cubes until the jar is half full of water.

3. Add three drops of blue food coloring to the jar with ice cubes.

4. Place both jars next to a sunny window.

5. After ten minutes, observe the two jars.

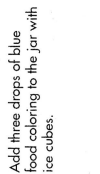

Explain Your Results

1. **Observe** What do you notice about the outside of the jars?

2. **Interpreting Data** Why do you think this happened?

Lab zone Activity

How can you tell that water is moving?

Materials

food coloring

mixing bowl with water

What to Do

1. Half-fill the bowl with water.

2. Add four drops of food coloring to the water. Do not stir it!

3. Observe how the food coloring moves through the water.

Explain Your Results

Infer How is the water in the bowl like water in the water cycle?

Process Skills

Observing helps you **infer** how the water in the bowl is similar to water in the water cycle.

Name _____

What happens when cold air meets warm air?

Record your observations of each jar below.

Jar with warm water and red food coloring	Jar with cold water and blue food coloring

Explain Your Results

1. **Observe** What do you notice about the outside of the jars?

_____

_____

_____

_____

2. **Interpreting Data** Why do you think this happened?

_____

_____

_____

_____

Notes for Home: Your child observed the process of condensation by observing a jar of warm water and a jar of cold water after ten minutes in sunlight.
Home Activity: With your child, observe grass in the morning when there is dew and explain that this is also condensation.

Name _____

How can you tell that water is moving?

Draw a picture of what you observed in the box below.

Explain Your Results

Infer How is the water in the bowl like water in the water cycle?

_____

_____

Notes for Home: Your child learned today that water is always moving just like in the water cycle.
Home Activity: With your child, discuss the importance of the water cycle and the stages of the water cycle.

Explore Which fossils match the plants and animals?

Explain Your Results

Communicate How did you match fossils to plants and animals?

_____

_____

_____

Notes for Home: Your child put together puzzles to understand how to associate fossil remains with once-living plants and animals.
Home Activity: Go online or take a trip to the library to find information and books about fossils with your child.

Investigate How can you make a model of a fossil?

❷ Tell about your fossil model and the shell.

How the Fossil Model and the Shell Are Alike and Different?	
How are they alike?	**How are they different?**

❹ Observe your partner's fossil model. Guess what it is.

_____

_____

Name _____

Explain Your Results

1. How did you **infer** what your partner's fossil model was?

_____

_____

_____

2. How do fossils give clues about living things?

_____

_____

_____

Go Further

What else could you do to make models of fossils? Make a plan and try it.

_____

_____

 Notes for Home: Your child made a model of a fossil by pressing a shell into clay and compared how this model of a fossil and an actual shell are alike and different.
Home Activity: Make a model of a leaf fossil by placing a leaf under a piece of paper and then rubbing a crayon over the paper. Compare how the model and the leaf are alike and different.

Name _____

© Pearson Education, Inc

Lab zone Activity

How do paleontologists dig for fossils?

Materials

pan of damp sand with hidden "fossils"

paint brush

plastic spoon

paper plate

craft stick

What to Do

1. **Use a Model** Dig for fossils carefully in the sand with a plastic spoon. Do this by slowly scraping and brushing the sand away until you find an object.

2. Once you find a fossil, use the spoon to remove it carefully from the sand.

3. Put the fossil on the paper plate.

4. Use the paintbrush to clean off the fossil.

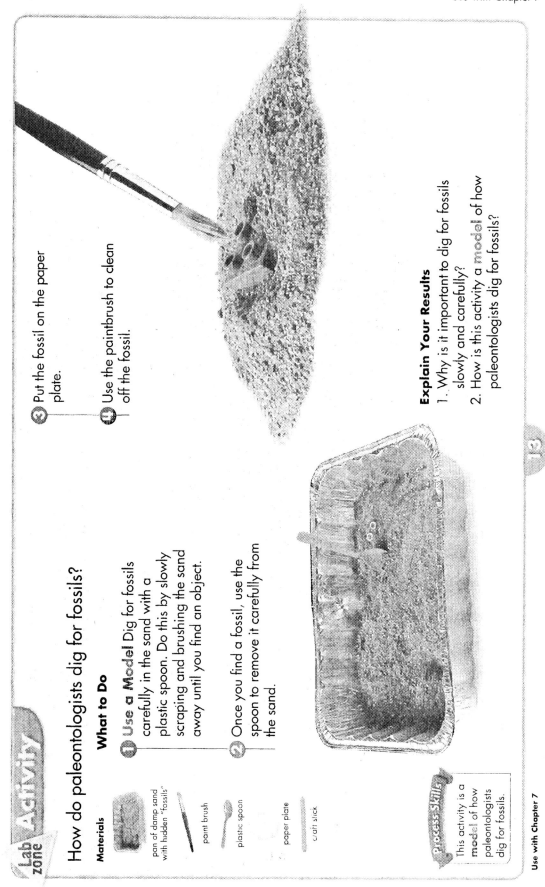

Explain Your Results

1. Why is it important to dig for fossils slowly and carefully?

2. How is this activity a model of how paleontologists dig for fossils?

Process Skills

This activity is a model of how paleontologists dig for fossils.

Lab zone Activity

How can you tell what made the tracks?

Materials

small objects

clay-dough

dowel

hand lens

Process Skills

You **interpret data** when you decide what item made each track

© Pearson Education, Inc

What to Do

1. Use the can or dowel to roll out the clay-dough.

2. Make sure your partner cannot see what you are doing. Then use different items to make tracks in the clay-dough. Make 5 to 10 tracks. You can use a whole side of an item or just part of it to make a track.

3. **Interpret Data** See if your partner can match each track with the item that made it. A hand lens can help you see details in the tracks and the items.

4. Switch with your partner and repeat the activity.

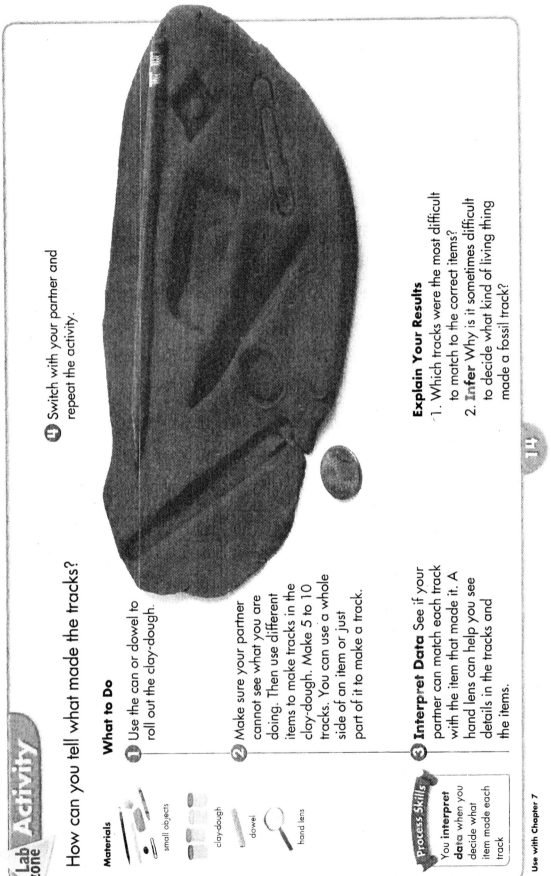

Explain Your Results

1. Which tracks were the most difficult to match to the correct items?

2. **Infer** Why is it sometimes difficult to decide what kind of living thing made a fossil track?

14

How do paleontologists dig for fossils?

Draw a picture of what you found during your dig.

Fossils Found

Explain Your Results

1. Why is it important to dig for fossils slowly and carefully?

_____

_____

2. How is this activity a **model** of how paleontologists dig for fossils?

_____

_____

_____

_____

 Notes for Home: Your child dug for fossils today and modeled what it is like to be a real paleontologist.
Home Activity: With your child, discuss the importance of finding fossils and how it helps us today.

How can you tell what made the tracks?

Draw a picture of what you observed in the box below.

Explain Your Results

1. Which tracks were the most difficult to match to the correct items?

_____

_____

2. Infer: Why is it sometimes difficult to decide what kind of living thing made a fossil track?

_____

_____

_____

Notes for Home: Your child made tracks in clay-dough and his or her partner had to guess what made the tracks. They realized why is it sometimes difficult to decide what kind of living thing made a fossil track.
Home Activity: With your child, look for animal tracks outside and try to match the tracks with what kind of animal made them.

© Pearson Education, Inc

Name _____

Experiment Does gravel, sand, or soil make the best imprint?

Ask a question.
Which will make the best imprint?

Make your hypothesis.

_____

_____

Plan a fair test.
Use the same amount of sand, gravel, and potting soil on each plate.

Do your test.
Follow steps 1 through 3.

Collect and record data.
Fill in the chart. Use an **✗** to show your results.

Which is the best imprint?			
	Best Imprint	**Some Imprint**	**No Imprint**
Gravel			
Sand			
Soil			

© Pearson Education, Inc.

Name _____

Tell your conclusion.

Does gravel, sand, or soil make the best imprint?
Which would make the best imprint fossil?

_____

_____

Go Further

What might happen if you use wet gravel, sand,
and soil? Try it and find out.

_____

_____

 Notes for Home: Your child made impressions of a shell in sand, potting soil, and
gravel to understand how fossils are formed.
Home Activity: Make impressions of small objects in the soil around your home
or at a park or at the beach.

Activity Book

Name _____

Explore What happens when oil is mixed with water?

Explain Your Results

1. What happened when you mixed the oil and the water?

_____

_____

2. Infer How could you separate oil from water?

_____

_____

Notes for Home: Your child combined oil and water and learned that these two liquids do not stay mixed.
Home Activity: Mix salad oil and vinegar and shake to mix. Observe the results. Ask your child to compare this mixture with the mixture of oil and water made at school.

© Pearson Education, Inc

Name _____

Investigate How can water change?

❶ Describe the liquid water.

_____

What is the temperature of the liquid water?

_____

❷ Describe the frozen water.

_____

What is the temperature of the water after being in the freezer?

_____

❸-❹ Predict What will happen to the water in a few hours? Will the temperature go up or down? What will happen to the outside of the cup?

_____

_____

_____

_____

Record the temperatures on this chart.

How does the temperature change?	
Time	**Temperature °C**
After 30 minutes	
After 1 hour	
After 2 hours	
After 3 hours	

Explain Your Results

1. Compare solid water to liquid water.

_____

_____

2. Predict How long will it take for the liquid water to evaporate?

_____

_____

Go Further What other types of matter change when they are frozen? Investigate to find out.

_____

_____

Notes for Home: Your child observed how the temperature and appearance of water changes as it freezes and thaws.
Home Activity: Observe how another liquid such as fruit juice changes when it is frozen. Then predict and note how long it takes to thaw.

Lab zone Activity

How are solids different from liquids?

Materials

milk and juice box

stapler and fruit

water and gelatin

blocks

2 index cards

What to Do

1. **Observe** each of the materials.

2. Discuss with your partner how they are alike and different.

3. **Classify** the items into two groups: solids and liquids.

4. Write a list of the items that are solids. Write another list of the items that are liquids.

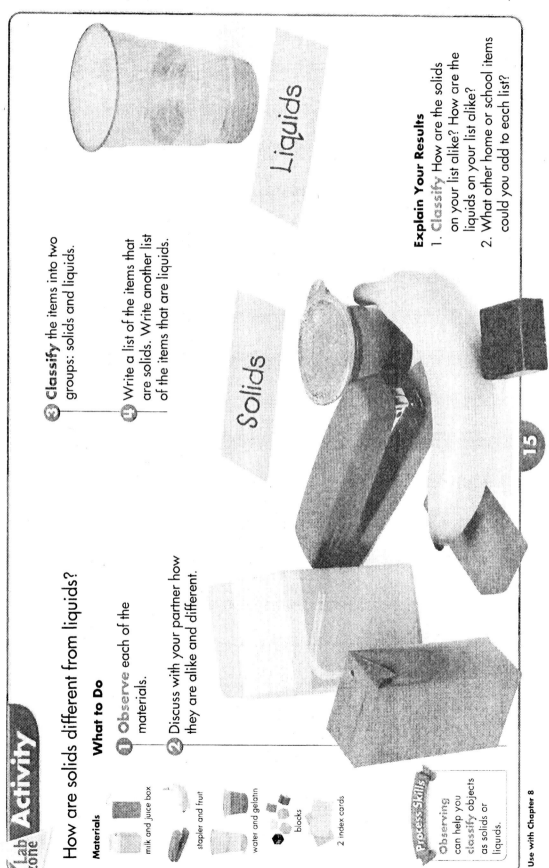

Liquids

Solids

15

Explain Your Results

1. **Classify** How are the solids on your list alike? How are the liquids on your list alike?

2. What other home or school items could you add to each list?

Process Skills

Observing can help you classify objects as solids or liquids.

Use with Chapter 8

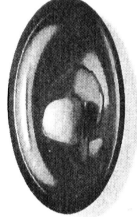

Explain Your Results

1. **Communicate** Tell, write, or draw what you did to make your ice cube melt fast.

2. **Predict** How could you melt an ice cube even faster?

16

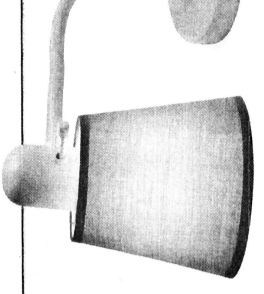

Lab zone Activity

How can you make an ice cube melt faster?

Materials

ice cube and plastic dish

lamp and paper towels

plastic bag

stopwatch or clock with second hand

Process Skills

Measuring how long it takes to melt an ice cube can help you **predict** how to melt the ice cube even faster.

What to Do

1. Put an ice cube in a dish.

2. Start the stopwatch.

3. Try to make your ice cube melt as fast as you can. Use the materials you have.

4. Measure the time it took to melt your ice cube.

Use with Chapter 8

© Pearson Education, Inc

How are solids different from liquids?

Classify the items by whether they are solid or liquid. List them in the correct category.

Solids	Liquids

Explain Your Results

1. **Classify** How are the solids on your list alike? How are the liquids on your list alike?

_____

_____

_____

_____

2. What other home or school items could you add to each list?

_____

_____

Notes for Home: Your child observed different materials and classified them by whether they were solid or liquid. They discussed how solids are similar and how liquids are similar.

Home Activity: With your child, find objects around the home that are solids and liquids. Do the solids have the same properties? Do the liquids have the same properties?

How can you make an ice cube melt faster?

Record the time it took your ice cube to melt in the chart below.

Time It Took Ice Cube to Melt

Explain Your Results

1. **Communicate** Tell, write, or draw what you did to make your ice cube melt fast.

_____

_____

2. **Predict** How could you melt an ice cube even faster?

_____

_____

Notes for Home: Your child experimented with how to make an ice cube melt fast. He or she measured the time it took to melt an ice cube and predicted how it could melt even faster.
Home Activity: With your child, discuss what inventions have been made to help speed up the process of heating.

Name _____

Explore Which color heats faster?

2 What are the temperatures on the two thermometers?

What is the temperature of the thermometer wrapped in white paper?

_____

_____

_____

What is the temperature of the thermometer wrapped in black paper?

_____

_____

_____

Explain Your Results

Infer How did color make a difference in temperature?

_____

_____

_____

Notes for Home: Your child learned that black paper absorbs more heat from light by wrapping one thermometer in white paper and one thermometer in black paper and placing both in the sun.
Home Activity: On a warm day, have your child wear a dark shirt outside and then change to a white shirt. Discuss which shirt feels cooler and why.

Name _____

Investigate How can you change light?

❸ Observe Draw what you see.

Changing Light

Name _____

Explain Your Results

1. What are some of the colors you saw?

_____

_____

2. Infer How does light change when it passes through water?

_____

_____

Go Further How would using colored paper change the colors you see? Try it and find out.

_____

_____

 Notes for Home: Your child held a flashlight above a pan of water to reflect light onto white posterboard to observe how the colors in light split as light passes through water.
Home Activity: Discuss rainbows, which are formed when light passes through raindrops, with your child. Look for rainbows on the next rainy day.

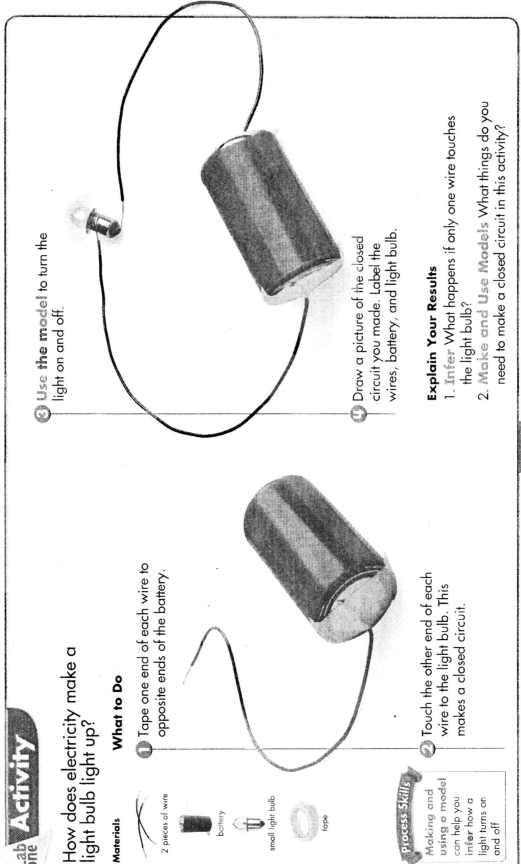

Activity

How does electricity make a light bulb light up?

Materials

2 pieces of wire

battery

small light bulb

tape

Process Skills

Making and using a model can help you infer how a light turns on and off

What to Do

1. Tape one end of each wire to opposite ends of the battery.

2. Touch the other end of each wire to the light bulb. This makes a closed circuit.

3. Use the model to turn the light on and off.

4. Draw a picture of the closed circuit you made. Label the wires, battery, and light bulb.

Explain Your Results

1. Infer What happens if only one wire touches the light bulb?

2. Make and Use Models What things do you need to make a closed circuit in this activity?

Use with Chapter 9

17

Lab Zone Activity

What gives off heat?

Materials

thermometer

lamp

What to Do

1. **Measure** Place the thermometer on the table. Make sure it is out of the sunlight. Wait two minutes. Record the temperature.

2. Turn on the lamp. Place the thermometer on the table about 10 centimeters from the bulb of the lamp. Wait two minutes and record the temperature.

3. Turn off the lamp. Place the thermometer in sunlight for two minutes. Record the temperature.

4. Hold the bottom part of the thermometer in your hand. Wait two minutes and record the temperature.

Explain Your Results

1. **Infer** What things give off heat, according to the results of this activity?

2. When you take the thermometer away from heat, the temperature of the thermometer goes down. What happens to the heat?

Process Skills

Measuring temperature can help you **infer** what things give off heat.

18

How does electricity make a light bulb light up?

In the box below, draw a picture of the closed circuit you made. Label the wires, battery, and light bulb.

Explain Your Results

1. Infer What happens if only one wire touches the light bulb?

_____

_____

2. Make and Use Models What things do you need to make a closed circuit in this activity?

_____

Notes for Home: Your child made a closed circuit using a battery, wire, and a light bulb.
Home Activity: With your child, discuss where you could find closed circuits in your house.

What gives off heat?

Record the temperatures you collected in the chart below.

Location	Temperature
Desk top	
Lamp	
Sunlight	
Your hand	

Explain Your Results

1. **Infer** What things give off heat, according to the results of this activity?

_____

_____

2. When you take the thermometer away from heat, the temperature of the thermometer goes down. What happens to the heat?

_____

_____

Notes for Home: Your child used a thermometer to measure the temperature of different things that give off heat.
Home Activity: With your child, use a thermometer to measure the temperature of various items to determine if they give off heat.

© Pearson Education, Inc

Name _____

Explore How can you measure force?

❶ How long is the rubber band when you pull it?

_____

_____

❷ Add 1 more book and pull. How long is the rubber band?

_____

_____

Explain Your Results

Communicate How are the measurements different?

_____

_____

Notes for Home: Your child pulled one book, and then two books, with a rubber band and observed that the rubber band stretched more. Your child used a rubber band to measure force.

Home Activity: Use a small narrow rubber band to pull small light objects and heavy objects. Observe that the rubber band stretches more as it moves heavier objects.

Name _____

Investigate What can magnets do?

1 **Interpret Data** What happens when the N and S ends of the magnets are pushed together? What happens when the N and N ends of the magnets are pushed together?

_____

_____

2 **Predict** which objects a magnet will pull. Try to pull each object.

_____

_____

3 Can a magnet pull through the things listed in the chart? Record what you **observe**.

Can a magnet pull through these things?				
	Air	Plastic Cup	Water	Paper
	gas	solid	liquid	solid
yes				
no				

Explain Your Results

1. What objects did you predict a magnet would pull? Which objects did it pull?

_____

_____

_____

2. Interpret Data What things could the magnet pull through?

_____

_____

Go Further

Can magnets pull objects through a piece of foil? Make a plan to find out.

_____

_____

_____

_____

Notes for Home: Your child learned what objects a magnet will repel and attract and that a magnet can attract a steel object through air space (gas), through water in a cup (liquid), and through a piece of cardboard (solid).
Home Activity: Look for household objects that a magnet will attract (objects containing steel or iron).

© Scott Foresman

Lab zone Activity

Do heavy objects fall faster than light objects?

Materials

classroom objects

Process Skills

You make **definitions** when you use **observations** to tell how objects fall.

What to Do

1. Choose two classroom objects. Hold each one in your hand. Which do you think is heavier?

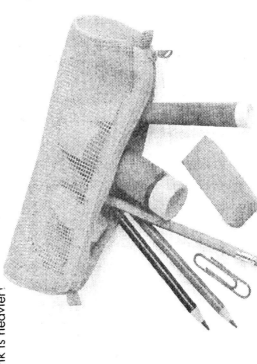

2. **Predict** which object will fall faster. Record your prediction.

3. Hold each object at the same height. Let go of them at the same time. **Observe** when each object hits the floor.

Explain Your Results

1. Was your prediction correct? If not, how was your observation different than your prediction?

2. **Make Definitions** What can you say about how heavy and light objects fall?

19

Name _____

Lab zone Activity

How do objects move on different surfaces?

Materials

washer

masking tape

ruler

sandpaper

piece of wood

What to Do

1. Place the washer on the table. Use a piece of masking tape to mark the position of the washer.

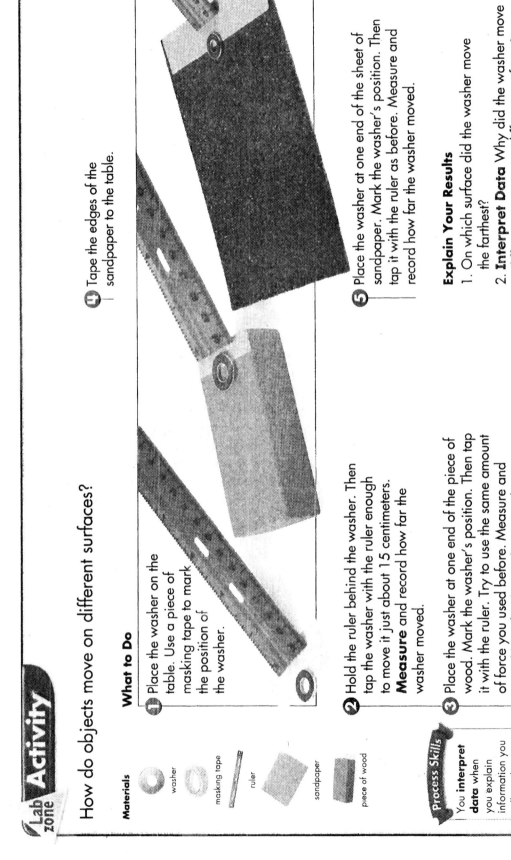

2. Hold the ruler behind the washer. Then tap the washer with the ruler enough to move it just about 15 centimeters. **Measure** and record how far the washer moved.

3. Place the washer at one end of the piece of wood. Mark the washer's position. Then tap it with the ruler. Try to use the same amount of force you used before. Measure and record how far the washer moved.

4. Tape the edges of the sandpaper to the table.

5. Place the washer at one end of the sheet of sandpaper. Mark the washer's position. Then tap it with the ruler as before. Measure and record how far the washer moved.

Explain Your Results

1. On which surface did the washer move the farthest?

2. **Interpret Data** Why did the washer move different amounts on different surfaces?

Process Skills

You **interpret data** when you explain information you collected.

20

Do heavy objects fall faster than light objects?

Write your prediction and actual outcome of which object will fall faster below in the chart.

Prediction	Actual Outcome

Explain Your Results

1. Was your prediction correct? If not, how was your observation different than your prediction?

_____

_____

_____

_____

2. Make Definitions What can you say about how heavy and light objects fall?

_____

_____

Notes for Home: Your child experimented with two classroom objects to see which would fall faster. Your child made a prediction and then tested it to find out how light and heavy objects fall.
Home Activity: With your child, make a prediction about other objects around the house to see which would fall faster. Test your predictions.

How do objects move on different surfaces?

Record how far the washer moved on each surface in the chart below.

Table	Wood	Sandpaper

Explain Your Results

1. On which surface did the washer move the farthest?

_____

2. Interpret Data Why did the washer move different amounts on different surfaces?

_____

_____

Notes for Home: Your child learned how friction causes objects to slow down their movement by measuring the distance a washer moved on a table, wood, and sand paper.

Home Activity: With your child, discuss how friction also causes heat. Rub your hands together to create friction and feel the warmth on your hands.

© Pearson Education, Inc

Name _____

Explore How can you make sound?

❶ Push down on one end of the ruler. Let go. **Observe**. What do you hear?

_____

❷ Slide the ruler back farther on the table. Push down on the ruler again. What do you hear?

_____

Explain Your Results

Observe Think about what you heard. How did the sound change when you moved the ruler back?

_____

Notes for Home: Your child placed a ruler on a table and pushed the free end to cause it to vibrate. Your child learned that vibration causes sounds.
Home Activity: Observe the sounds caused by vibration around your home, such as the hum of the refrigerator.

Name _____

Investigate How can you change sound?

3 Fill in the chart.

	Is the sound loud or soft?
Hard plucks	
Gentle plucks	

Infer What changes the sound?

_____

_____

4 Move the pencils apart. **Predict** whether the sound will be higher or lower.

_____

© Pearson Education, Inc

5 Fill in the chart.

	Is the sound high or low?
Pencils close	
Pencils far apart	

Explain Your Results

1. What made the sound high? What made the sound loud?

_____

_____

_____

2. Infer How could you make a quiet, low sound?

_____

_____

_____

Go Further

What other things can you do to change the sound? Investigate to find out.

_____

 Notes for Home: Your child learned how to change volume and pitch of sound by playing a musical instrument made by stretching rubber bands around a cardboard box.
Home Activity: Use large and small plastic food containers to make musical instruments. Use containers with lids as drums or fill containers with seeds or dried beans to make instruments to shake.

© Pearson Education, Inc

Lab zone **Activity**

How can you describe sound?

Materials

4 glass jars

pitcher of water

food coloring

metal spoon

What to Do

1. Add a few drops of food coloring to the pitcher of water. Mix the water with the spoon.

2. Fill the jars with different amounts of water. Line up the jars in order from least full to most full.

3. Gently tap the middle of each jar with the spoon. Don't tap too hard. **Observe** the sounds.

Process Skills

You can **observe** by listening as well as by seeing.

Explain Your Results

1. **Communicate** Describe the pitch of each sound.

2. How did you change the sounds from each jar?

21

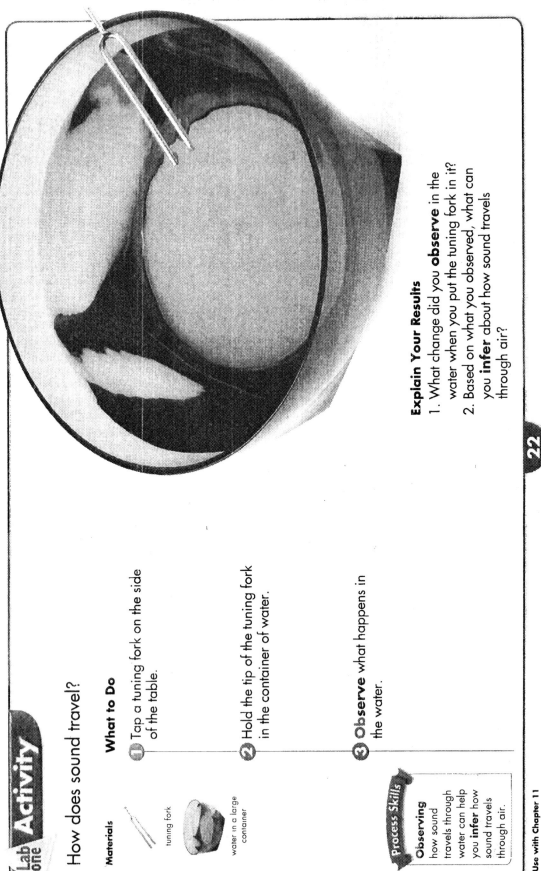

Activity

How does sound travel?

Materials

tuning fork

water in a large container

What to Do

1. Tap a tuning fork on the side of the table.

2. Hold the tip of the tuning fork in the container of water.

3. **Observe** what happens in the water.

Process Skills

Observing how sound travels through water can help you **infer** how sound travels through air.

Explain Your Results

1. What change did you **observe** in the water when you put the tuning fork in it?

2. Based on what you observed, what can you **infer** about how sound travels through air?

22

How can you describe sound?

Explain Your Results

1. Communicate Describe the pitch of each sound.

_____

_____

2. How did you change the sounds from each jar?

_____

_____

Notes for Home: Your child tapped on glasses filled with different water levels and was able to describe the sounds he or she heard.
Home Activity: With your child, fill glasses at home with different water levels and make up a song by tapping on the side of the glasses with a spoon.

© Pearson Education, Inc

How does sound travel?

Record your observation in the box below.

[box]

Explain Your Results

1. What change did you **observe** in the water when you put the tuning fork in it?

_____

2. Based on what you observed, what can you **infer** about how sound travels through air?

_____

_____

Notes for Home: Your child observed how sound travels through water by watching a vibrating tuning fork make ripples in water. Your child inferred that sound moves through air in small waves.
Home Activity: With your child, discuss why we are not able to see the sound vibrations in the air.

© Pearson Education, Inc.

Experiment What kinds of objects reflect light clearly?

Ask a question.

What kinds of objects reflect light clearly?

Make your hypothesis.

Do smooth and shiny objects reflect light clearly? Tell what you think.

_____

Plan a fair test.

Make sure the objects are the same size. Use the same flashlight.

Do your test.

Write your **observations** in the chart on the next page.

1 Is the mirror smooth? Is it shiny?

2 Does the mirror reflect light clearly?

3 Test the other objects. Do steps 1 and 2 again.

Name _____

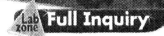
Collect and record your data.

	Is it smooth? yes or no	**Is it shiny?** yes or no	**Does it reflect light clearly?** yes or no
mirror			
paper			
wrinkled foil			
wrinkled paper			

Tell your conclusion.

Do smooth and shiny objects reflect light clearly? How do you know?

_____

_____

_____

Go Further

What might happen if you test other classroom objects? Experiment to find out.

_____

_____

 Notes for Home: Your child used a flashlight to shine light on objects to find out which objects will reflect light onto a wall.
Home Activity: Place smooth and shiny household objects next to a light-colored wall. Shine a flashlight on them to see if the object will reflect light onto the wall.

Name _____

Explore What causes day and night?

Explain Your Results

How does your **model** show day and night?

_____

_____

_____

_____

_____

Notes for Home: Your child observed models to understand that when the Sun lights the side of Earth we are living on, it is daytime; and when that part of Earth turns away from the Sun it is nighttime.

Home Activity: Observe the Sun in the sky in the morning and evening of one day. Discuss how the Sun's position changed because Earth has moved.

Investigate How can you make a model of a constellation?

❸–❹ Observe your constellation. Draw and name your constellation.

My Constellation

Explain Your Results

1. Tell about your constellation. How is your model like a real constellation?

_____

_____

How is it different from a real constellation?

_____

_____

2. Make a definition of a constellation.

_____

_____

_____

Go Further

How else could you make a model of your constellation? Investigate to find out.

_____

_____

_____

Notes for Home: Your child learned to identify and make a constellation by shining a light through holes in paper.
Home Activity: Look for constellations in the night sky. In the winter, look for three stars in a row that make up Orion's belt. Look for the Big Dipper (seven stars that form the shape of a ladle).

Lab zone Activity

What causes the seasons?

Materials

globe

black and yellow dot stickers

flashlight

books

Process Skills

You use a model to infer where Earth is in space during each season.

What to Do

1. Place a black dot sticker on the globe where you live.

2. **Make and Use a Model** Lay the flashlight on a stack of books so that the light shines on the middle of the globe. The flashlight stands for the Sun.

3. Place the globe so that it is tilted away from the flashlight. Turn on the flashlight. Use a yellow dot to mark the center of where the light hits the globe. This is position A.

4. Move the globe a quarter of the way around the flashlight.

5. Turn the flashlight to shine on the globe. Spin the globe so that the yellow dot faces the flashlight. Use another yellow dot to mark the center of where the light hits the globe. This is position B.

6. Repeat steps 4 and 5 two more times. Now you have placed the globe in four different positions—A, B, C, and D.

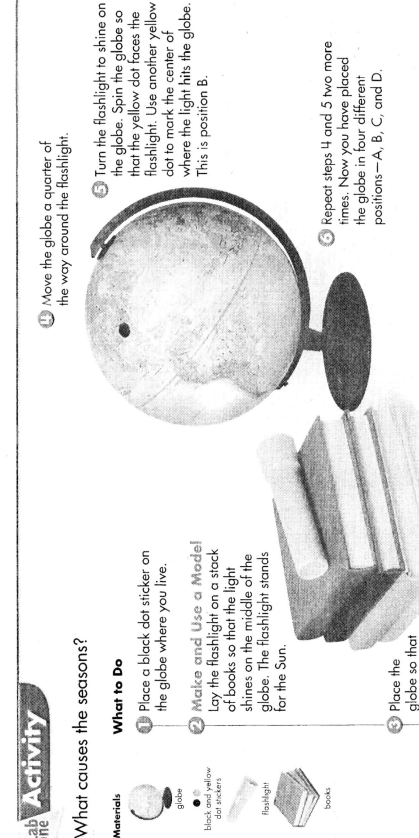

Explain Your Results

1. **Infer** Each position stands for Earth at the beginning of a different season. Which position is the beginning of winter where you live? Which position is the beginning of summer?

2. What causes the seasons to change where you live?

23

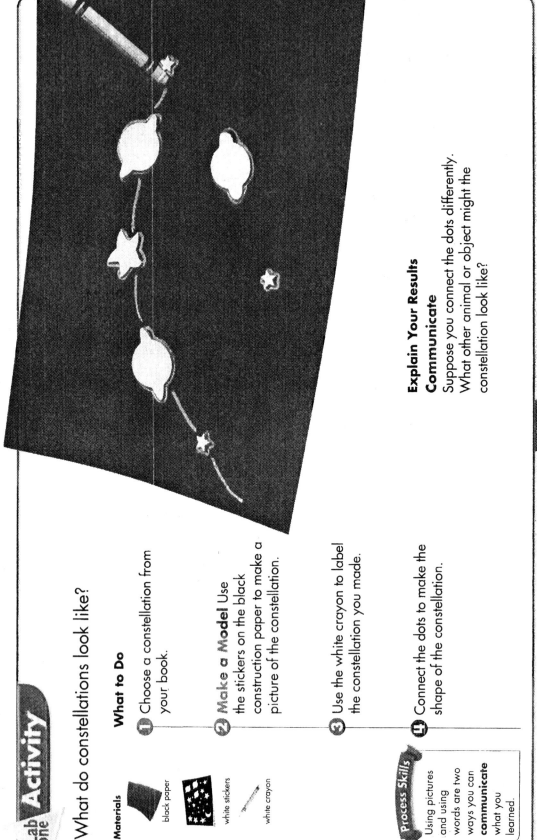

Lab zone **Activity**

What do constellations look like?

Materials

black paper

white stickers

white crayon

Process Skills

Using pictures and using words are two ways you can **communicate** what you learned.

What to Do

1 Choose a constellation from your book.

2 **Make a Model** Use the stickers on the black construction paper to make a picture of the constellation.

3 Use the white crayon to label the constellation you made.

4 Connect the dots to make the shape of the constellation.

Explain Your Results
Communicate
Suppose you connect the dots differently. What other animal or object might the constellation look like?

24

© Pearson Education, Inc

What causes the seasons?

Explain Your Results

1. **Infer** Each position stands for Earth at the beginning of a different season. Which position is the beginning of winter where you live? Which position is the beginning of summer?

_____

_____

_____

2. What causes the seasons to change where you live?

_____

_____

Notes for Home: Your child learned about Earth's rotation around the Sun and what causes the different seasons. He/she learned about the Sun's position on Earth when it is the beginning of the summer and winter seasons where we live. **Home Activity:** With your child, watch the Sun as it rises and sets. Note the direction the Sun rises and sets each day.

What do constellations look like?

Explain Your Results

Communicate Suppose you connect the dots differently. What other animal or object might the constellation look like?

_____

_____

Notes for Home: Your child made up his/her own constellation, made a model of it using glow in the dark dot stickers, and gave it a name.
Home Activity: With your child, go outside at nighttime and look for a constellation in the sky.

© Pearson Education, Inc

Name _____

Explore How can you move the ball?

Explain Your Results

Communicate Tell how you solved the problem.

_____

_____

_____

_____

_____

_____

_____

Notes for Home: Your child solved the problem of getting a metal ball in a cup using a magnet, ruler, pencil, and spoon.
Home Activity: Encourage your child to think up solutions to everyday problems such as how to clean up his or her room (for example, use a rug to pull objects across the floor or use posterboard as a chute to pour puzzle pieces into a box).

Investigate How can you make a maze?

1 How can you make a maze that a marble can follow? Draw your plan here.

3 **Predict** Will your maze work? _____

4 Test your maze. Then move the tubes to make the maze work better.

5 Test your maze two more times.

Test your maze.	
Test	**Did the marble follow the maze?**
1	
2	
3	

Explain Your Results

Communicate Tell how the parts of your maze work together.

_____

_____

_____

_____

Go Further

How can you make your marble move in a different way? Investigate to find out.

_____

_____

Notes for Home: Your child used paper tubes in different ways to make a variety of mazes. Your child used trial and error to retape the tubes in a pattern to successfully get a marble through the paper-tube maze.
Home Activity: Have your child recreate his or her maze at home using masking tape to attach paper tubes to cardboard.

Name _____

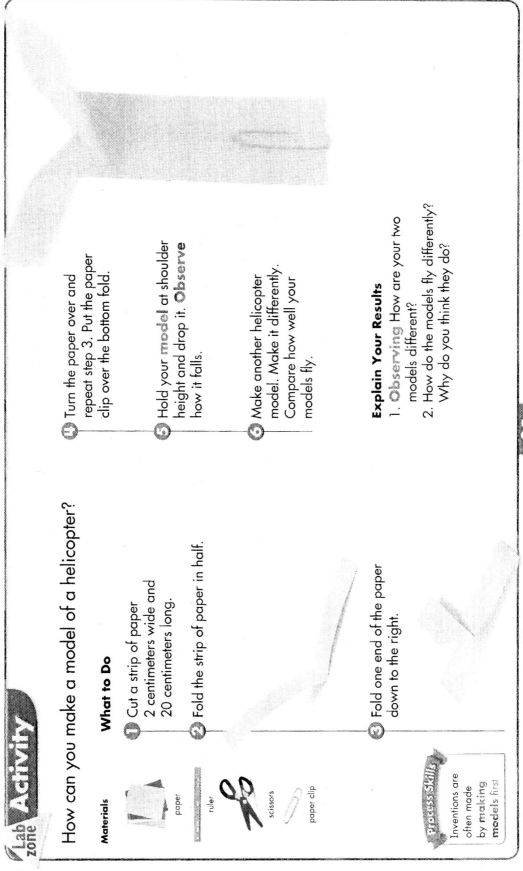

How can you make a model of a helicopter?

Materials

paper

ruler

scissors

paper clip

What to Do

1. Cut a strip of paper 2 centimeters wide and 20 centimeters long.

2. Fold the strip of paper in half.

3. Fold one end of the paper down to the right.

4. Turn the paper over and repeat step 3. Put the paper clip over the bottom fold.

5. Hold your model at shoulder height and drop it. **Observe** how it falls.

6. Make another helicopter model. Make it differently. Compare how well your models fly.

Explain Your Results

1. **Observing** How are your two models different?

2. How do the models fly differently? Why do you think they do?

Process Skills

Inventions are often made by making models first.

Use with Chapter 13

25

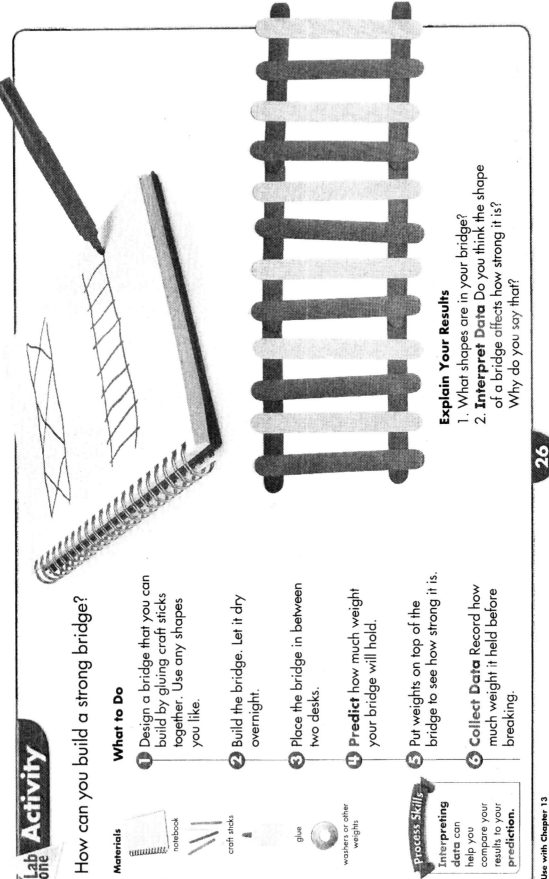

Lab zone **Activity**

How can you build a strong bridge?

Materials

notebook

craft sticks

glue

washers or other weights

Process Skills

Interpreting data can help you compare your results to your prediction.

What to Do

① Design a bridge that you can build by gluing craft sticks together. Use any shapes you like.

② Build the bridge. Let it dry overnight.

③ Place the bridge in between two desks.

④ **Predict** how much weight your bridge will hold.

⑤ Put weights on top of the bridge to see how strong it is.

⑥ **Collect Data** Record how much weight it held before breaking.

Explain Your Results

1. What shapes are in your bridge?

2. **Interpret Data** Do you think the shape of a bridge affects how strong it is? Why do you say that?

26

How can you make a model of a helicopter?

Draw a picture of your two model helicopters in the box below.

Explain Your Results

1. Observing How are your two models different?

_____

_____

2. How do the models fly differently? Why do you think they do?

_____

_____

_____

Notes for Home: Your child made two models of helicopters and compared how they flew differently because of the way that they were made.
Home Activity: With your child, make models of helicopters and a target. Try to get your model helicopters to land on the target. Which model worked the best and why?

How can you build a strong bridge?

Record your prediction and actual outcome of how much weight your bridge will hold in the chart below.

Prediction: How Much Weight?	Actual Outcome: How Much Weight?

Explain Your Results

1. What shapes are in your bridge?

_____

2. **Interpret Data:** Do you think the shape of a bridge affects how strong it is? Why do you say that?

_____

_____

Notes for Home: Your child built a model of a bridge and made a prediction of how much weight it would hold. Then your child tested his or her bridge and recorded how much weight it could hold. Your child learned that the shape of a bridge affects how strong it is.

Home Activity: With your child, make a bridge out of clay and out of craft sticks. Test the bridge to find out how much weight it can hold.

Experiment Which tissue is the strongest?

Ask a question.

Are tissues that cost more stronger than tissues that cost less?

Make your hypothesis.

_____

_____

_____

Plan a fair test.

Use the same amount of water to wet each tissue. Use 3 different brands of tissue. Each should have a different cost.

Do your test.

Follow steps 1 through 6.

Collect and record data.

Show how many marbles it takes to break the tissue and how much the marbles weigh. Record your data on page 138.

Name _____

Tissue Cost	How many marbles?	How many grams?
Most		
Middle		
Least		

Tell your conclusion.

Which tissue is the strongest?

_____

_____

_____

Go Further

What if you used less water to wet each tissue?
Try it and find out.

_____

_____

 Notes for Home: You child tested how many marbles a wet tissue can support to find out which of three tissues is the strongest.
Home Activity: Try this experiment at home. Stretch three types of tissue over jars with rubber bands. Wet the tissue and place a number of small heavy objects (such as rocks) on each tissue until it breaks.

Teacher Resources and Answers

Activity Masters

Class Record Sheets with Activity Rubrics T35–T64

Directed, Guided, Full Inquiry and Activity Flip Chart

Activity Rubric Masters T65–T94

Directed, Guided, Full Inquiry and Activity Flip Chart

Process Skill Activity Answers . . . T95–T101

Activity Recording Sheet Answers T102–T131

Directed, Guided, Full Inquiry, and Activity Flip Chart

Scaffolded Inquiry

Dr. Karen Ostlund, Director
UTeach, College of Natural Sciences
The University of Texas at Austin
Austin, Texas

The **Continuum of Inquiry** is a series of developmental stages. Students progress through these stages to learn the skills and knowledge necessary to engage in inquiry. The sequence of the stages in the Continuum of Inquiry is described on page 4.

The Processes of Inquiry	Question	Predict or Formulate Hypotheses	Investigate	Collect & Organize Data
Beginning Stage Directed Inquiry	Students use question provided by the teacher, materials, or some other source.	Students are given a prediction for conducting a descriptive investigation or a hypothesis for conducting an experiment.	Students are given the procedures and materials to conduct an investigation (descriptive investigation or experiment).	Students follow step-by-step procedures provided by the teacher, materials, or some other source to collect and organize data into tables, graphs, and/or charts.
Transitional Stage Guided Inquiry	Students are guided to refine and clarify questions developed with input from the teacher, materials, or some other source.	Students are guided to make a prediction for descriptive investigations or construct a hypothesis for experiments and revise predictions and/or hypotheses if necessary.	Students are given suggestions for procedures and materials that could be used to conduct an investigation (descriptive investigation or experiment).	Students are given instructions to collect data and tables, graphs, and/or charts are recommended to organize the data collected.
Final Stage Full Inquiry	Students investigate a question that can be answered by doing descriptive investigations or experiments.	Students develop logical/reasonable predictions and/or hypotheses.	Students devise a plan that takes all the variables into account and conduct an investigation (descriptive investigation or experiment).	Students decide how and what data to collect and construct tables, graphs, and/or charts to organize the data collected.

The chart below shows stages in the development of the processes of inquiry. Classrooms may be at different stages in this development process, but the ultimate goal is to reach Full Inquiry.
Students: The Beginning Stage has the least amount of student self-direction and Final Stage has the most student self-direction.
Teachers: The Beginning Stage indicates the most direction from the teacher and/or material and Final Stage indicates the least direction from the teacher and/or materials.

Analyze and Draw Conclusions	Formulate Explanations	Propose Scientific Explanations	Communicate Findings
Students are given instructions on how to analyze the data, and guided to draw a conclusion to answer the question being investigated.	Students take synthesized data and are given step-by-step directions to formulate their explanation.	Students are given scientific explanations.	Students are given step-by-step procedures for communicating findings and justifying a provided explanation with evidence from the investigation.
Students are given suggestions on how to analyze the data on their own and draw conclusions to answer the question being investigated.	Students are guided in the process of formulating explanations from the data they collected, analyzed, and synthesized.	Students are guided to reliable sources of scientific explanations and asked to compare this information to their explanations and make any necessary revisions.	Students are given guidelines for communicating findings and justifying their explanations with evidence from their investigation.
Students determine what evidence is needed, analyze the collected data, and draw conclusions to answer the question being investigated.	Students formulate their explanation after analyzing and synthesizing the data they collected.	Students independently examine scientific explanations from reliable sources and use the information to revise and strengthen their explanations.	Students use logical reasoning to communicate findings and justify their explanations with evidence from their investigation.

Activity Book Teacher's Guide

Developmental Stages of Inquiry

Directed Inquiry

❏ The beginning stage, **Directed Inquiry**, is teacher- or materials-directed. It provides a structured model of the inquiry process. Without this type of support and guidance, students cannot progress to asking and answering scientific questions independently.

❏ Directed Inquiry introduces students to the essential features of inquiry, and helps students reflect on the characteristics of the processes in which they are engaged.

❏ Directed Inquiry provides the foundation upon which subsequent stages of inquiry are built. These explorations are designed to provide students with the experiences necessary to learn and practice the processes of inquiry.

Guided Inquiry

❏ In the second stage, **Guided Inquiry**, the teacher moves from the role of director to facilitator. Students continue to refine their inquiry skills based on the foundation developed during the Directed Inquiry explorations.

❏ During Guided Inquiry, students have the opportunity to practice skills of inquiry with greater independence. Students are encouraged to think about variables, and they learn to plan for all the variables that may affect the outcome of an investigation.

❏ Guided Inquiry focuses student attention on learning particular science concepts. Students build science literacy and improve confidence in their abilities to do inquiry.

Full Inquiry

❏ **Full Inquiry** is one of the ultimate goals of science literacy. To conduct full inquiry, students must be able to apply the skills and knowledge developed in the previous stages of the Continuum of Inquiry.

❏ According to the National Research Council (1996), Full Inquiry takes place if the following essential features of inquiry are present.
  ○ Questions are scientifically oriented
  ○ Learners use evidence to evaluate explanations
  ○ The explanations answer the questions
  ○ Alternative explanations are compared and evaluated
  ○ Explanations are communicated and justified

❏ Full Inquiry is modeled in Scott Foresman *Science* ©2006 to provide a framework so that students can conduct their own investigations. After practicing the thinking processes as they follow the model of a full inquiry experiment, students are encouraged to pose scientifically oriented questions and investigate independently.

Because Scott Foresman *Science* provides scaffolded inquiry, students will be able to attain reaching the goal of conducting independent inquiry. Without the developmentally appropriate framework provided by scaffolded inquiry, an unrealistic burden rests on the teacher (Colburn, 2004). Moving from teacher-directed to teacher-facilitated to student-directed inquiries allows for a continuously deepening understanding of the skills and knowledge fundamental to conducting inquiry. Therefore, the cycle of Directed, Guided and Full Inquiry is repeated throughout the Scott Foresman *Science* program.

Students must be provided with the scaffolding to engage in full inquiry. They need to practice how to plan and conduct an investigation. Planning begins with posing a question or problem that can be investigated. Then the conditions of the investigation need to be set up (which variables will remain the same, which will be changed, and what outcome or effects will provide the results). Next the investigation is conducted, data is collected and analyzed, an explanation is formulated and compared to scientific knowledge, and the explanation is communicated and justified.

References

Colburn, Alan (2004). Inquiring Scientists Want to Know. *Educational Leadership, 62*(1), 63–66.

National Research Council (1996). *National Science Education Standards.* Washington, DC: National Academy Press.

National Research Council (2000). Steve Olson and Susan Loucks-Horsley, eds. Committee on the Development of an Addendum to the National Science Education Standards on Scientific Inquiry, National Research Council. *Inquiry and the 'National Science Education Standards': A Guide for Teaching and Learning.* Washington, DC: National Academy Press.

Activity Book Teacher's Guide

Teaching Safety in the Classroom

Dr. Jack. A. Gerlovich, Professor
Science Education/Safety
Drake University
Des Moines, Iowa

"Safety is a fundamental concern in all experimental science. Teachers of science must know and apply the necessary safety regulations in the storage, use, and care of the materials used by students. They adhere to safety rules and guidelines that are established by national organizations...as well as by local and state regulatory agencies. They work with the school and district to ensure implementation and use of safety guidelines for which they are responsible, such as the presence of safety equipment and appropriate class size. Teachers also teach students how to engage safely in investigations inside and outside the classroom."

—National Science Education Standards, 1996

Safe procedure is part of sound scientific inquiry. Activities throughout Scott Foresman *Science* reinforce and extend science concepts using materials and procedures that are generally safe when used as directed. Students who use this program learn not only how to safely investigate the topics at hand; they also develop safety habits that will serve them well in future scientific endeavors.

Throughout Scott Foresman *Science*, students learn that simple, safe materials can be used effectively to investigate science concepts. Safety reminders regarding procedure are given in the Student's Edition whenever appropriate. These include "Be careful!" symbols and references to cover goggles on appropriate pages. The Teacher's Edition includes specific safety tips for activities and demonstrations. If properly implemented, these guidelines can help assure a safe science teaching and learning setting for teacher and students.

General safety tips for the elementary science classroom

- ❏ Teachers should conduct annual audits of safety problems and inform the administration of problems in writing.
- ❏ All emergency telephone numbers (police, fire department, nurse, hospital, poison control center, and so on) should be posted with a telephone easily and quickly accessible.
- ❏ Safety should be incorporated into all teacher lesson plans and student lab/activity reports.
- ❏ Prior to using any equipment or substances, teachers should be certain they understand the proper function and hazards associated with the use of those items. This information should be communicated to the students.
- ❏ The proper use of appropriate eye protective equipment that meets the American National Standards Institute (ANSI Z87.1) standards should be demonstrated to students. These should be worn whenever using the potential for eye injury exists, including: use of caustic chemicals, equipment, glassware, or projectiles. Even relatively safe items such as rubber bands and balloons can cause eye injury and warrant the use of eye protection. All protective eye equipment should be sanitized before it is worn by students.
- ❏ To prevent students from interfering with each other and to assist the safe exit of students from the room in case of an emergency, teachers should assure that rooms are not overcrowded, that students understand exit procedures, and that aisles are kept uncluttered.

- ❏ Teachers should periodically conduct practice drills with students to address foreseeable emergencies. For example, students might practice exiting the room due to an emergency.

- ❏ Unless you know the outcome is safe, you should never mix substances "just to see what happens."

- ❏ All equipment should be properly stored. Dangerous items should be kept under lock and key.

- ❏ Whenever possible, plastic items should replace glass. If glass containers are essential, temperature- and break-resistant glassware should be used.

- ❏ To prevent slipping and falls, any liquids spilled on tile or hardwood floors should be wiped up immediately.

- ❏ To verify that all applicable science safety issues are understood by students, the teacher may want to have students state them or write them in their own words. The teacher should discuss any necessary adjustments with students before allowing students to proceed with the laboratory/activity.

Teachers should be aware of applicable federal, state, and local laws (especially as they relate to teachers' tort duties and obligations), codes (fire, building, electrical, plumbing, and so on), professional science education standards (facilities, equipment, procedures, and so on), and relevant guidelines from professional organizations that apply to the activities being performed. For field trips, it is imperative that teachers visit the site (to check for hazards) before involving students there and they should use appropriate forms to inform parents. Refer to the following materials for other information about classroom safety.

Resources

Biehl, J. T.; L. L. Motz; S. S. West. (1999) *NSTA Guide to School Science Facilities*, National Science Teachers Association, Arlington, VA.

Kwan, Terry; Juliana Texley. (2002). *Exploring Safely: A Guide for Elementary Teachers*, National Science Teachers Association, Arlington, VA.

National Science Teachers Association (1997) *NSTA Pathways to the Science Standards, Elementary School Edition*, National Science Teachers Association, Arlington, VA.

National Research Council (1996) *National Science Education Standards*, National Academy Press, Washington, D.C.

How to Plan a Science Fair

I. Introduction and Overview

What is a science fair?

A science fair creates opportunities for direct student involvement in the processes of inquiry. The purpose of a science fair project is to engage students in the process of asking and answering their own questions. Scott Foresman *Science* provides scaffolded inquiry to build knowledge and skills required to engage in this type of full inquiry.

Why do a science fair?

The science fair can be one of the most exciting parts of the entire school curriculum. As students explore the mysteries and marvels of the world in which they live, they also come to appreciate the work of scientists. Moreover, seeing one another's projects stimulates the student's own inquiries. Interests kindled during a science fair often carry students well beyond their projects and their school days.

What are the "payoffs" for doing a science fair?

The important part of science fairs is participation, not winning. The real goal is to stimulate students' curiosity about the world and thereby encourage their participation. If that goal is met, everyone who enters wins. Every participant should receive some recognition—whether it be notice in the school newspaper, a letter of appreciation, or a certificate—and students should be able to look forward to that acknowledgement, even as they begin their work.

How can a fair be used for assessment?

A science fair provides several levels of assessment opportunity. Comparing student results with the objectives incorporated in a good set of guidelines furnishes the teacher with a useful diagnostic tool. The same process is of further value in the student's own, continuing self-evaluation. Parents also are able to follow and evaluate the student's progress at home. Requiring a written summary report provides yet another tool for a final assessment.

Establish criteria that will help teachers, families, and students alike to plan, execute, and evaluate projects. The Sample Judging Form on page 13 suggests a number of key points.

Before students begin they should be furnished with guidelines. Emphasize that students are not competing against each other but will be rewarded for creativity and thoroughness.

What tips or practical suggestions will reduce stress?

Advance planning: Your school's faculty and staff can work as a team to begin early preparations for the science fair. Fit background activities to the curriculum and build enthusiasm for the fair. Assign people to supervise and assist at setup time, during the fair, and at the post-fair dismantling. Decide on a panel for judging student projects. If you invite guest panelists or advisors from the local scientific community, allow plenty of time for them to respond.

Publicity: Post flyers advertising the science fair. Send a notice to the local newspaper and to students' families.

Special Equipment/Materials: Identify well in advance any special needs, such as access to electrical outlets or water and unusual construction requirements or materials.

Safety: Some equipment or materials may require special safety measures. Speak to students about the safe handling of scientific materials. Have staff on hand during the fair to monitor safety.

II. The Science Fair Project

What is it?

Depending on the developmental level of your students, a science fair project can include the following types of investigations:

Systematic observations or descriptive investigations should answer "what would happen if" and "measuring questions" such as how much. Variables that could affect the outcome of the investigation are identified and decisions are made to plan for each one.

Experiments answer comparison questions. In an experiment, one variable is changed (manipulated) and a responding variable is observed and/or measured. All other variables that could affect the outcome of the investigation are controlled or held constant.

Research projects begin similarly. Students work to conclusions by using primary sources, such as written materials or personal interviews. Students develop interesting ways to interpret, summarize, and present their research.

Demonstrations allow students to show a certain scientific fact, principle, phenomenon, process, or practical application at work.

Apparatus, used for an experiment or demonstration, may in its own right be the center of a project. A student may wish to investigate its origins and evolution, or its exact workings.

Collections may be formed around any type of animal, plant, or mineral specimen. A collection need not be comprehensive, but it should present a cohesive group of objects that help to fully explain some aspect of science. The objects should be catalogued in a systematic fashion, clearly labeled, and attractively displayed.

What are the parts of a science fair project?

Display Backdrop A backboard provides a setting, as well as a support for titles, introductions, labels, and flat art such as diagrams, photographs, or drawings. All information should be legible.

Some materials that work well as backdrops are pegboard, plywood, corkboard, particleboard, and foam board. (Cardboard and poster board are not sufficiently rigid to stand on their own.)

The Exhibit The exhibit comprises all aspects of a student's investigations and provides the viewer with a firsthand look at the project's scope. Collections or experiment materials are set up with sufficient explanatory support to tell a clear and complete story. Avoid clutter. Organize and set up the display in a logical and attractive manner. Liquids, chemicals, and smelly substances should be tightly sealed in containers. Animals should not be used because there are strict regulations about using animals in research. Prepare a safety checklist for the students.

Written Report

The written report is an integral component of every science project; science calls for all data and observations to be recorded in writing. The report also demonstrates the student's grasp of the topic. A final benefit for the student is one of hindsight. Reviewing data for the written report may help to firm up or revise the student's conclusions.

The report should be neatly typed and bound. The following elements should be included: title page with researcher's name and grade; table of contents; statement of the problem; question investigated; hypothesis or prediction; materials; procedure; observations and results; explanation; research; conclusion; and next question. Upper grades may also prepare a bibliography.

III. The Mechanics of a Science Fair

Engage the Students

The memory from the preceding year of a well-run science fair with full student participation is a powerful enticement for a good student effort in the present science fair. Teachers also must prepare students well and offer them strong guidance through the planning and preparation stages. Make a great deal of information available to the students.

Some students may be interested to know about science fairs on state or national levels. Avoid misdirection and frustration, however, and emphasize above all the correct use of scientific methods and the development of successful thinkers, rather than trophies and awards. Finally, invite the students to contribute their own ideas for the fair, and solicit family involvement, as well.

Integrate the Fair with Other Subjects

Keep the team approach alive. Teachers and staff can work together and align the objectives of the science fair with those of the curriculum. A whole curriculum approach increases the effectiveness of the science fair schoolwide.

Ties can be made between the written report and a language arts lesson. Math skills can be reinforced in the measurement or estimation phases of a project. Social studies may be involved in investigating scientists, and art skills can be used in preparing the presentation. Possible connections seem limitless.

Involve the Whole School

Expand the team! Generate enthusiasm in a well-planned, pre-fair buildup. Ask the principal to visit classes and talk about past science fairs. See if the school newspaper can run articles on students' preparations for the fair (and later on, reports of the fair's outcome—which will lay the groundwork for the following year).

The school librarian might prepare a special book display. Enlist the art teacher and interested students to make posters and flyers for the science fair. Social studies teachers might lead discussions about TV science programming that students may see on TV. The librarian and the language arts teachers may join forces with reading specialists to present literature with science themes.

Engage the Community

Students may wish to promote the science fair schoolwide by inviting community members active in science to participate in classroom panel discussions. Invite student family members and others in the community to bring in scientific instruments or examples from natural history collections for display at school.

Organize a Schedule

There is much to be done, if a science project is to be done well. Stress to families and students that a successful science project needs several weeks of work. Projects must be planned well in advance to allow students sufficient time for the necessary research, construction, writing, and the final assembly of the project. Ideally, you should consider a 12-week timetable. Suggestions for a minimum 6-week plan are presented on page 12.

IV. How to Create Successful Projects

General Recommendations

You may wish to prepare a short version of the following recommendations and encourage students to keep it at the beginning of their project notebooks.

- **Does the project represent the student's own work?**
  While students may receive help in investigating and designing their projects, the final efforts must be theirs alone.

- **Is the project the result of careful planning?**
  A hastily constructed project undermines the value of the science fair. Students must be encouraged to develop a systematic plan that will be carried out over a period of time.

- **Does the project demonstrate the student's creativity and resourcefulness?**
  Students should be permitted to use their own ideas for the design and implementation of their project.

- **Does the project indicate a thorough understanding of the chosen topic?**
  Students need to investigate their topics as completely as possible. This requires work over an extended period of time.

Specific Information about Science Fair Projects

As students come close to the end of their projects, ask them to check for the following points:

- **Does the project include a notebook, written record, or final report?**
  The display should include a written summary of the investigation, separate from the written report, which viewers may see as a part of the student's work.

- **Does the project include a number of visual aids?**
  Encourage students to use photographs, charts, diagrams, tables, or drawings, as they seek to make the project more interesting.

- **Is the project sturdy, well constructed, and safe?**
  Help students use proper materials and to be careful in assembling their projects. Size limitations and permanence are important factors. Check electrical items or chemicals to ensure the safety of observers. Remind them to follow safety guidelines.

- **Is the display three-dimensional?**
  Make sure students arrange all their samples, apparatus, collections, or other items in an attractive manner before a backdrop display.

- **Is all information accurate and all sign lettering neat?**
  All written data should be presented neatly and accurately. All questions about the data should be resolved before including them in a report or on the display.

V. How to Help Students Set Their Criteria for Choosing a Topic

The student's own motivation will be the critical factor in the successful completion of a project. Teachers and families can help provide direction, but the final choice is the student's. It may help students to pose questions in ways that help them refine their choices.

Remind students that, most of all, their projects should truly interest them.

Interests
- What kinds of things do you enjoy doing?
- What area of science interests you the most?
- What are your hobbies or free time activities?
- What kind of books and TV shows do you like?
- What are your special skills or talents?

Difficulty Level
- How hard will this topic be for you to understand?
- Are you familiar with this topic, or is it brand new?
- Will you need to gather a lot of outside information?
- Will you be able to work on this project for 6 (or 12) weeks and still be interested?
- What special tools or apparatus do you think you will need?

Time
- Will you be able to spend some time on this project every week?
- How long will it take to gather information?
- Will you need to set up a special schedule to complete all the things you need to do?
- Do you have enough free time at home to work on the project?

Materials
- What special materials will you need for this project?
- Do you have those materials at home or will you need to buy them?
- Will you need to order materials or buy them in local stores?
- Will your materials be costly?
- Will you need help constructing something complicated?

Guidance
- How much help will you need with your project?
- Will you need to consult experts in your chosen field?
- Will you have to build the display unit on your own?

Safety
- Are there any dangers from equipment or materials associated with your project?
- Will you be able to follow all safety rules in putting your project together?

Methods of Presentation
There are six basic ways in which students may present their projects: systematic observations, experiments, demonstrations, research, collections, and apparatus. As students think about areas of science that interest them, the mode of presentation may also help narrow their project selection. Refer the students to these categories, which are presented on p. 8, and review them together.

VI. Project Sampler

Project Ideas

The lists that follow offer a diverse selection of topics to show students the range of possibilities. Students do not need to be confined to a particular list, and keep in mind that students in different grades may choose the same topic yet develop their projects in simpler or more complicated ways.

Primary grade topics:

- The phases of the Moon
- Seeds: growing and caring for them
- Healthy eating habits
- Pulleys, force, and energy
- A water cycle
- Comparing machines and their uses
- Sound and matter
- Magnets and the Aurora Borealis
- Plants and food
- Animal babies: birth and growth

Intermediate grade topics:

- How changing the fulcrum affects a lever
- How crystals are formed
- Construct a model of the eye showing its different parts.
- The types of jobs bees have in a honeybee colony
- Why animals hibernate
- The behaviors of earthworms
- Whether the wind can be used to make electricity in the area where we live
- Study a local bird population and graph your findings.
- Make a model of an atom.
- Compare photosynthesis and respiration.

Sample Planning Calendar

Week 1 Choose a topic, list resources, and contact experts.

Week 2 Begin putting project notebook together and start collecting or experimenting.

Week 3 Begin work on display, take photos, complete research, and begin written report.

Week 4 Continue collecting or experimenting, and set up tests.

Week 5 Write second draft, and design and assemble graphs and charts.

Week 6 Write final report, set up display at home to test, and transport project to fair site and test it.

VII. Sample Judging Form

Display/Display Materials

Creativity
(30 points)   Score _____
- ☐ Are the materials presented imaginatively and attractively?
- ☐ Is the project original, distinctive and inventive?
- ☐ Is interesting and appropriate information included in the display?

Scientific Thought
(30 points)   Score _____
- ☐ Is the experiment designed to answer a question and is the question clearly stated?
- ☐ Have appropriate resources been consulted and cited?
- ☐ Has a systematic plan been stated?
- ☐ Is there a clear and adequate solution or conclusion?
- ☐ Is the project notebook provided with the display?
- ☐ Does the student show a clear understanding of all the facts and theories?

Thoroughness
(15 points)   Score _____
- ☐ Is the project complete and does it represent sufficient use of time and resources?
- ☐ Is the problem/theory thoroughly answered/pursued?
- ☐ Does the project include a display unit, three-dimensional items, and a written report?

Skill
(25 points)   Score _____
- ☐ Does the project represent the student's own work?
- ☐ Does the project represent quality workmanship and extensive planning?
- ☐ Is the data clearly, neatly and legibly presented?
- ☐ Is the project clear and understandable?

Total for Display/Display Materials   _____

Written Report

Introductory Pages
(5 points)   Score _____
- ☐ Is there a complete title page?
- ☐ Is there a complete table of contents?

Statement of Purpose and Hypothesis
(20 points)   Score _____
- ☐ Does the statement of purpose pose a question that pertains to the project?
- ☐ Does the hypothesis answer the statement of purpose and tell what the student is trying to determine with the project? (Experiment only)

Research and Bibliography
(25 points)   Score _____
- ☐ Is research complete and thorough, and does it pertain to the topic?
- ☐ Does it represent a diversity of sources?
- ☐ Is the bibliography complete and clear?

Materials and Procedures
(20 points)   Score _____
- ☐ Are all materials listed?
- ☐ Are materials sufficient?
- ☐ Are procedures listed in a logical order?
- ☐ Could you use the procedures to replicate the experiment/project?

Observations and Conclusions
(30 points)   Score _____
- ☐ Do the observations sequentially indicate what was done in the report?
- ☐ Did the student choose the best/clearest format for recording the observations?
- ☐ Does the conclusion answer the purpose?
- ☐ Does the conclusion adequately explain the result? (Experiment only)
- ☐ Is it clear and lengthy enough?

Total for Written Report _____

Total for Project
(200 possible points)   _____

Certificate of
Participation

This certificate is hereby presented to _____

For participation in the **Annual Science Fair**

school _____

principal _____

teacher _____

date _____

Family Science Night: A Blueprint for Success

The Problem:

You're convinced that parental involvement is an untapped resource at your school and you'd like to connect with families in a more exciting way than the traditional outreach vehicles—annual curriculum night and the monthly newsletter—allow. However, your workload is heavy and you don't have time to spend on an event that is unrelated to your busy curriculum.

The Solution:

Family Science Night!

Family Science Night is an engaging way to bring students and three of their most influential forces—family, teachers, and peers—together for a fun evening of science activity and interaction. And you don't even have to be a science expert to run such an event! After all, parents don't come to Family Science Night for their science degree—they come for their kids! The main purpose of the evening is one of outreach, an opportunity to shape positive attitudes and create greater science awareness while simultaneously promoting parent, child, and teacher interactions. The benefits from a series of successful Family Science Nights can be significant!

The information on the following pages provides a blueprint for you to create and customize your own Family Science Night initiative. Basic information about organizing and staging a Family Science Night is provided on page 16. The **SHAPE** formula for success on page 17 suggests a way to structure your evening based on observations of successful techniques used by teachers experienced in facilitating Science Nights throughout the country. Activity suggestions and Invitation templates furnish time-saving ideas and artwork.

Research shows that engaged families who support and reinforce what a child is being taught in school can make a positive difference in that child's school performance. **Family Science Night** provides an opportunity for families to support and participate in learning together. We hope these materials will aid your efforts to convince families to participate with you in this all-important task.

Organizing and Staging a Family Science Night: Frequently Asked Questions

Who will be in charge?

The general director can be a teacher, a school administrator, or a parent volunteer. This person will research and plan the evening, using the **SHAPE** formula as a guide for success. The director will also need to be comfortable leading the parent-child teams through an evening of interaction and activity.

Who will help the director to distribute materials?

It is helpful to have several volunteers on hand to pass out materials and answer questions at the event. These volunteers can be teachers or parents. (Approximately one volunteer for every ten families in attendance works well.) Student volunteers can assist with the advance preparation of materials kits.

Where will the event be held in the school?

The school cafeteria is an ideal place to hold an event. Long cafeteria tables work well for the recommended events, and there is usually easy access to distribute participating families between two locations, such as a gym and a cafeteria. In this case, the handouts given to the families upon their arrival can be color-coded to direct them to a particular location.

Does a Family Science Night cost money?

Yes, but the amount depends entirely upon the way you choose to structure your event. Typical expenditures are for materials needed for activities, door prizes for participants (optional), or rental and transportation to bring in more elaborate setups, such as a StarLab (optional). Funding may come from school budgets or donations from parent/ teacher organizations or local businesses. Providing a meal—such as having pizzas donated—helps bring families out.

Who will purchase and organize supplies prior to the event?

Usually the Science Night director tests supply samples and performs a trial run of each proposed activity. Then a parent/ teacher organization, parent volunteers, or teacher volunteers may assist with the purchase and organization of supplies for the event. Student volunteers can follow a prepared sample and fill plastic bags with materials for the actual kits.

How will the event be advertised?

Typically, an invitation flyer is sent home to advertise the event. This flyer should include the following information:

- The date and time of the event

- The location of the event

- A brief description with any other helpful information a parent may need to know

- RSVP slip with a deadline for return

SHAPE Your Family Science Night for Success!

Start with everyday science... Consider your audience's perspective. Sometimes parents (more than their children!) are intimidated by the subject matter of science. They might not have had a successful experience in their own school days or perhaps they just think that they aren't as up-to-date as they should be. A good way to engage your audience and put them at ease for the evening is to first demystify the subject matter. Use examples to point out that science is all around us and we are all scientists making science-related decisions every day whether we realize it or not!

Have fun with it... As you make the point that science is all around, try to introduce a little humor into your examples. Laughter is a wonderful antidote to anxiety and injecting a little fun into your opening remarks sets the stage for a great evening. Try *The Science of Everyday Life* (Viking Press), a book by Jay Ingram. There are many books and websites that are great resources for interesting science topics. Just think of a question related to your science night theme and have a little fun with it!

Arrange interesting interactions... After your audience is engaged you want to take the next step to "involve." Simple activities that lend themselves to collaboration work best. For example, you might want to challenge each group to design a paper airplane that they think will fly the farthest. Be prepared to jump-start some groups if they're having difficulty, but try not to stifle the spontaneity as this is where the fun (and learning) begin!

Another successful interaction technique is to arrange for a "high-interest" item to be brought in. For example, one school collaborated with its local community college to bring in a portable astronomy lab to help them study the solar system on Family Science Night. Take advantage of the skills and connections your own parents may have to offer...it will save you time and money.

Pause for wrap-up... Every good teaching event requires closure and Family Science Night is no exception. Allow for some time to discuss what you've all learned together. Discuss the science of course, but don't forget to acknowledge the participants in the event as well. Congratulate adult family members for making the time to come out with their kids. Let them know you appreciate their commitment to education and their positive role modeling. Make sure the kids feel appreciated as well. Praise for a job well done is a great incentive for the future!

End with enrichment... Some families will be excited to do more together. Make that opportunity easy for them by providing a list of books, projects, websites, etc. that are appropriate for family exploration. It's also a great idea to give a simple activity assignment for families to do at home together in preparation for the next Family Science Night. For example, ask families to determine how many drops of water they can fit on a penny. Instruct the families to bring their results to the next Family Science Night. This not only helps bridge interest from one event to the next but it also provides an opportunity for families to continue to explore together!

Balloon Busters

Created by Anne Grall Reichel, Coordinator,
Lake County Educational Services, Grayslake, IL

Invitation to Participants: Your challenge is to invent a strategy for busting a balloon. You have 30 minutes to create and test your strategy.

Get Ready

1. First lay out the string in your bag to measure the distance (one meter).

2. Place your balloon at one end of the measured distance. You can use tape to secure the balloon.

3. Set up two or three blocks at the opposite end from the balloon.

4. Rest one end of the ruler on the top of the blocks. The other edge of the ruler should be resting on the table just at the end of the distance measured with the string. You have created a ramp.

Get Started

5. Use the other materials in the bag to build a chain reaction that will burst the balloon.

6. Use the energy of the ball rolling down your ramp to start the chain reaction that will burst the balloon at the other end.

7. You may use any combination of the materials in the bag to achieve the goal.

8. Be prepared to demonstrate or draw your solution(s).

NOTES TO FACILITATOR

- As families work on the problem, visit the tables offering words of encouragement. Carry additional balloons in your pocket in case balloons burst accidentally.

- Allow 20–30 minutes for participants to complete the activity.

- When groups burst the balloon, you can either give them another balloon and ask them to find an alternative solution or give them a large piece of paper and a marker to draw their first solution.

- Drawings can be taped along the wall in the hall so that families can observe the diverse ways in which materials were used to solve the problem. A parent volunteer or teacher assisting with the evening can quickly tape the papers up in the hallway.

- When the majority of family groups have completed the task, draw the entire group back together. (A microphone is very helpful at this point.)

Sharing Results

- Discuss the diverse solutions the groups invented and emphasize the role of trial and error in working towards a solution. If the groups have drawn their solutions encourage others to visit the display in the hall at the end of the evening. Emphasize that each group invented a diverse system using the same materials.

Activity Wrap-up

- Direct groups to place materials back in the zip lock bags.

Science Night

When:

Where:

Additional Information:

RSVP

_____ Yes, we will attend.

Number of People _____

_____ **No**, we will not attend.

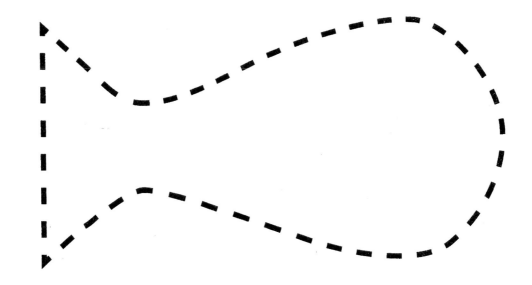

Kelp crabs and sea urchins eat kelp.

kelp

Octopuses and sea otters eat kelp crabs.

Kelp crabs eat kelp.

- -

kelp crab

© Pearson Education, Inc

Sea otters, sea stars, and sea gulls eat sea urchins.

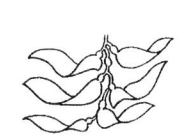

Sea urchins eat kelp.

- -

sea urchin

Sea gulls and sea otters eat sea stars.

Sea stars eat sea urchins.

- -

sea star

© Pearson Education, Inc

Sea gulls eat sea stars and sea urchins.

sea gull

Octopuses eat kelp crabs.

octopus

Orcas eat sea otters.

Sea otters eat kelp crabs, sea urchins, and sea stars.

- -

sea otter

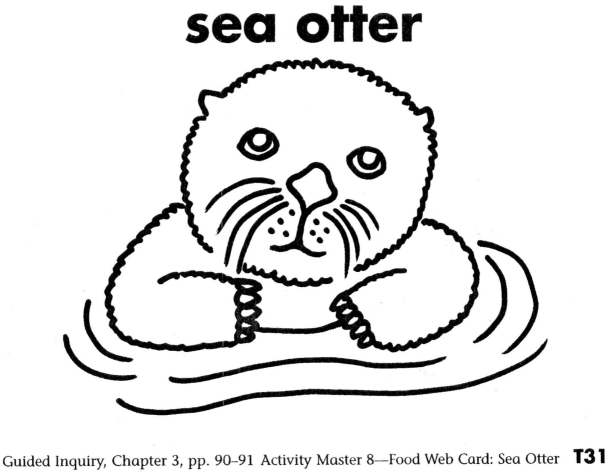

Orcas eat sea otters.

orca

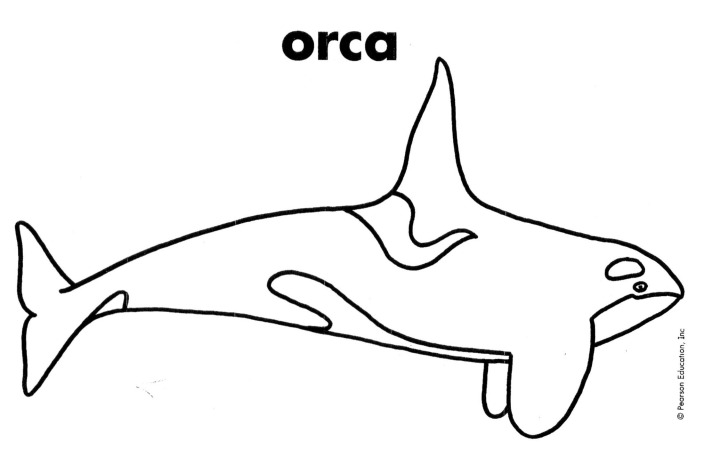

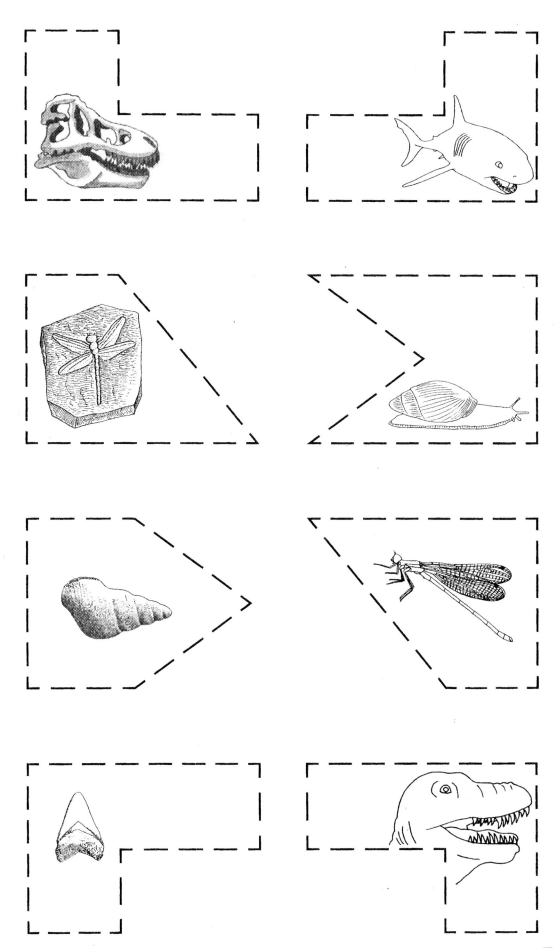

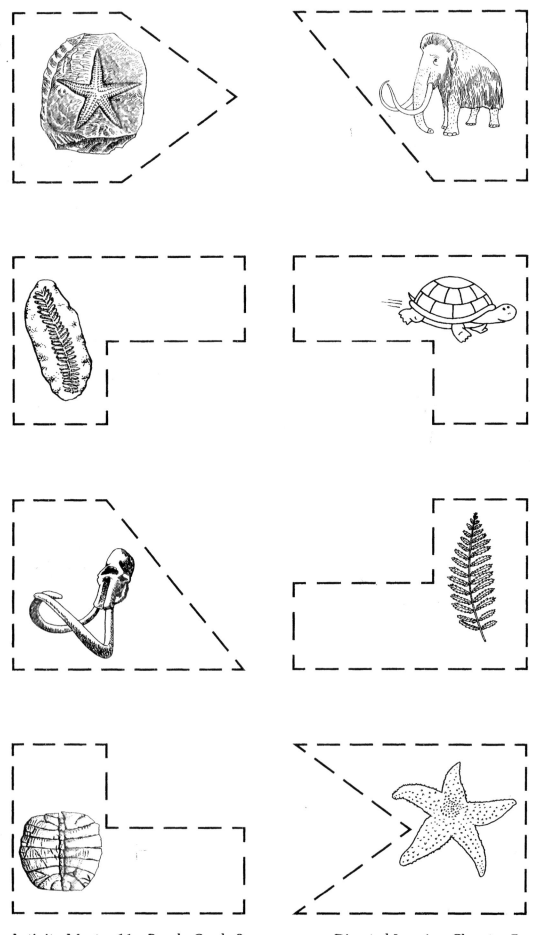

Directed Inquiry, Chapter 7, p. 204

Use the following activity scoring to assess students' performance

Scoring Key

4 correct, complete, detailed	**3** partially correct, complete, detailed	**2** partially correct, partially complete, lacks some detail	**1** incorrect or incomplete, needs assistance

Directed Inquiry (p. 4)
Explore: Do plants need water?

Scoring Criteria																		
Student followed directions to complete activity.																		
Student described what happened to celery without water for one day.																		
Student **predicted** the result of adding water to wilted celery.																		
Student described how and why wilted celery changed after placing it in water.																		
Student **predicted** what will happen if the celery is taken out of the water.																		
Score																		
total points																		
% equivalent																		

Guided Inquiry (pp. 26–27)
Investigate: Do plants need light?

Scoring Criteria																		
Student followed directions to complete this activity.																		
Student stayed on-task during this activity.																		
Student **observed** both plants daily.																		
Student recorded **observations** by filling in the chart with drawings.																		
Student **inferred** that a plant will die if it does not get sunlight.																		
Score																		
total points																		
% equivalent																		

Use the following activity scoring to assess students' performance

Scoring Key

4 correct, complete, detailed	**3** partially correct, complete, detailed	**2** partially correct, partially complete, lacks some detail	**1** incorrect or incomplete, needs assistance

Activity Flip Chart (p. 1)
What are the parts of a flowering plant?

Scoring Criteria

Student followed instructions to complete this activity.																					
Student **made a model** of a flowering plant.																					
Student labeled the parts of the model of the flowering plant he/she made.																					
Student **communicated** the four parts of the flowering plant.																					
Student **communicated** how each part helps the plant.																					
Score																					
total points																					
% equivalent																					

Activity Flip Chart (p. 2)
How are a cactus and a fern alike and different?

Scoring Criteria

Student followed instructions to complete this activity.																					
Student **observed** the cactus with the hand lens.																					
Student **communicated** how the plants were alike.																					
Student **communicated** how the plants were different.																					
Student correctly recorded data in the chart.																					
Score																					
total points																					
% equivalent																					

Activity Rubrics
Chapter 2

Use the following activity scoring to assess students' performance

Scoring Key

4 correct, complete, detailed	**3** partially correct, complete, detailed	**2** partially correct, partially complete, lacks some detail	**1** incorrect or incomplete, needs assistance

Directed Inquiry (p. 36)

Explore: How are worms and snakes alike and different?

Scoring Criteria

Student followed directions to complete this activity.

Student **made a model** of a worm.

Student **made a model** of a snake.

Student felt the worm model and told how it felt.

Student felt the snake model and told how it felt.

Score	% equivalent
total points	

Guided Inquiry (pp. 56–57)

Investigate: How can an octopus use its arms?

Scoring Criteria

Student followed directions to complete this activity.

Student **predicted** the number of suction cups needed to open the jar.

Student figured out how to place the suction cups.

Student recorded the **prediction** and result in a bar graph.

Student **communicated** how the suction cups were used.

Score	% equivalent
total points	

Activity Rubrics
Chapter 2

Use the following activity scoring to assess students' performance

Scoring Key

| **4** correct, complete, detailed | **3** partially correct, complete, detailed | **2** partially correct, partially complete, lacks some detail | **1** incorrect or incomplete, needs assistance |

Activity Flip Chart (p. 3)
How does camouflage help an animal survive?

Scoring Criteria

Student followed instructions to complete this activity.

Student drew a picture of an animal.

Student **made a model** of a habitat to camouflage the animal he/she drew.

Student **communicated** why it is hard to find the animal in its habitat.

Student **inferred** how camouflage helps the animal to survive

Score																						
total points																						
% equivalent																						

Activity Flip Chart (p. 4)
Why does a backbone have many parts?

Scoring Criteria

Student followed instructions to complete this activity.

Student **made a model** of a backbone using string and beads.

Student compared how the string of beads moves and how a pencil moves.

Student **inferred** if his/her backbone was more like the string of beads or a pencil.

Student **communicated** how a backbone with many parts helps an animal move.

Score																						
total points																						
% equivalent																						

Use the following activity scoring to assess students' performance

Scoring Key	**4** correct, complete, detailed	**3** partially correct, complete, detailed	**2** partially correct, partially complete, lacks some detail	**1** incorrect or incomplete, needs assistance

Directed Inquiry (p. 68)
Explore: What does yeast need to grow?

Scoring Criteria

Student followed directions to complete this activity.

Student stayed on-task during the activity.

Student **estimated** how long it took for bubbles to appear after water and sugar were added to yeast.

Student **observed** the effect of mixing yeast, water, and sugar.

Student **inferred** that yeast bubbles when it uses sugar and water as food.

Score	
total points	
% equivalent	

Guided Inquiry (pp. 90–91)
Investigate: How can you model a food web?

Scoring Criteria

Student followed directions to complete activity.

Student tossed a ball to another student.

Student drew the **model** of the food web and recorded the organisms' names.

Student **inferred** what the food web lines represented.

Student explained how the food web **model** represents a real life food web.

Score	
total points	
% equivalent	

Use the following activity scoring to assess students' performance

Scoring Key

| **4** correct, complete, detailed | **3** partially correct, complete, detailed | **2** partially correct, partially complete, lacks some detail | **1** incorrect or incomplete, needs assistance |

Activity Flip Chart (p. 5)
What is a food chain?

Scoring Criteria

Student followed instructions to complete this activity.

Student used materials appropriately to complete this activity.

Student drew pictures of a leaf, an insect, a small bird, and an owl.

Student glued the pictures and arrows on a sheet of large paper to make a food chain.

Student **made a definition** to **communicate** what the food chain showed.

Score	
total points	
% equivalent	

Activity Flip Chart (p. 6)
How does a bird make a nest?

Scoring Criteria

Student followed instructions to complete this activity.

Student **made a model** of a bird nest.

Student illustrated the bird nest.

Student **communicated** what plant parts are used to make a bird nest.

Student **inferred** how a nest helps birds.

Score	
total points	
% equivalent	

Activity Book

Use the following activity scoring to assess students' performance

Scoring Key	**4** correct, complete, detailed	**3** partially correct, complete, detailed	**2** partially correct, partially complete, lacks some detail	**1** incorrect or incomplete, needs assistance

Directed Inquiry (p. 100)
Explore: Which hand do different children use to write?

Scoring Criteria

Student followed directions to complete this activity.

Student stayed on-task during the activity.

Student identified the hand with which the student writes.

Student taped a hand cutout correctly on the graph.

Student **inferred** that some people are left-handed and some are right-handed from data on graph.

Score	total points	% equivalent

Guided Inquiry (pp. 122–123)
Investigate: How does a caterpillar grow and change?

Scoring Criteria

Student **observed** a butterfly's life cycle every day for three weeks.

Student **collected** data every day for three weeks.

Student **predicted** that a butterfly would emerge from the chrysalis.

Student drew pictures to show the stages of a butterfly's development and described how it changed.

Student **inferred** that the butterfly developed inside the chrysalis.

Score	total points	% equivalent

Use the following activity scoring to assess students' performance

Scoring Key

4 correct, complete, detailed	**3** partially correct, complete, detailed	**2** partially correct, partially complete, lacks some detail	**1** incorrect or incomplete, needs assistance

Activity Flip Chart (p. 7)
How common are some traits?

Scoring Criteria

Student followed instructions to complete this activity.

Student **observed** classmates.

Student collected data about the traits classmates had.

Student **communicated** the trait the least amount of classmates had.

Student **communicated** the trait the most classmates had.

Score	
total points	
% equivalent	

Activity Flip Chart (p. 8)
What happens when a seed germinates?

Scoring Criteria

Student followed instructions to complete this activity.

Student **observed** the radish seeds each day for four days.

Student collected data each day for four days to fill in the chart.

Student **communicated** how he/she knew the seeds germinated.

Student **predicted** what the seeds would look like after a week.

Score	
total points	
% equivalent	

Activity Book

Scoring Key

4 correct, complete, detailed	**3** partially correct, complete, detailed	**2** partially correct, partially complete, lacks some detail	**1** incorrect or incomplete, needs assistance

Use the following activity scoring to assess students' performance

Full Inquiry (p. 132)
Experiment: Which bird beak can crush seeds?

Scoring Criteria

Scoring Criteria																							
Student made a **hypothesis** about the type of bird beak that can crush seeds.																							
Student tested the hypothesis by **making and using models** of a heron's beak and a cardinal's beak.																							
Student **collected** and recorded **data** that showed the results of testing the bird beak **models.**																							
Students told which **model** crushes a piece of straw.																							
Student **inferred** which bird beak can crush seeds.																							
Score	total points																						
	% equivalent																						

Use the following activity scoring to assess students' performance

Scoring Key

4	correct, complete, detailed
3	partially correct, complete, detailed
2	partially correct, partially complete, lacks some detail
1	incorrect or incomplete, needs assistance

Directed Inquiry (p. 140)
Explore: How are soils different?

Scoring Criteria																	
Student followed directions to complete this activity																	
Student **observed** the appearance, smell, and texture of sandy soil and potting soil.																	
Student **observed** the absorptive qualities of sandy soil and potting soil.																	
Student described how sandy soil and potting soil are alike.																	
Student described how sandy soil and potting soil are different.																	

Score																	
total points																	
% equivalent																	

Guided Inquiry (pp. 160–161)
Investigate: How do worms change the soil?

Scoring Criteria																	
Student followed directions to complete this activity.																	
Student **observed** the compost bags for three weeks.																	
Student **collected data** by making drawings in chart for three weeks.																	
Student **inferred** that worms "ate" the leaves and incorporated the leaves into the soil.																	
Student reported that the bag without worms had more leaves after three weeks.																	

Score																	
total points																	
% equivalent																	

Activity Rubrics
Chapter 5

Scoring Key

4 correct, complete, detailed	3 partially correct, complete, detailed	2 partially correct, partially complete, lacks some detail	1 incorrect or incomplete, needs assistance

Use the following activity scoring to assess students' performance

Activity Flip Chart (p. 9)
How does erosion affect land?

Scoring Criteria

Student followed instructions to complete this activity.

Student **observed** how the water affected the height of the hill.

Student recorded data about the height of the hill before erosion, the estimated height of the hill after erosion, and the height of the hill after erosion.

Student **made an inference** about how rain affects land.

Student **estimated** the height of the hill after it had been eroded.

Score	
total points	
% equivalent	

Activity Flip Chart (p. 10)
How can you reuse something?

Scoring Criteria

Student followed instructions to complete this activity.

Student understood what it means to reuse something.

Student **communicated** how he/she would reuse the container.

Student inferred how you could change one of the containers to use it in another way.

Student observed the different containers to see what they were used for.

Score	
total points	
% equivalent	

Use the following activity scoring to assess students' performance

Scoring Key

4 correct, complete, detailed	**3** partially correct, complete, detailed	**2** partially correct, partially complete, lacks some detail	**1** incorrect or incomplete, needs assistance

Directed Inquiry (p. 172)
Explore: How much rain falls?

Scoring Criteria

Student followed directions to complete this activity.

Student stayed on-task during the activity.

Student marked 12 lines 1 centimeter apart on a strip of masking tape.

Student numbered the lines from 1 to 12.

Student **inferred** how the rain gauge could be used to measure rainfall.

Score	
total points	
% equivalent	

Guided Inquiry (pp. 194–195)
Investigate: How can you measure weather changes?

Scoring Criteria

Student checked the rain gauge and thermometer for one week.

Student **collected data** on a chart to show daily rainfall and temperatures for one week.

Student summarized the weather for the week.

Student **classified** each day as rainy or not rainy.

Student **interpreted data** by telling weather changes from day to day.

Score	
total points	
% equivalent	

Scoring Key

4 correct, complete, detailed	**3** partially correct, complete, detailed	**2** partially correct, partially complete, lacks some detail	**1** incorrect or incomplete, needs assistance

Use the following activity scoring to assess students' performance

Activity Flip Chart (p. 11)
What happens when cold air meets warm air?

Scoring Criteria

Student followed directions to complete this activity.

Student **observed** the outside of each jar after ten minutes.

Student **communicated** the differences between the jars after ten minutes.

Student **inferred** that water vapor in warm air condenses onto the outside of cold glass jars or glasses.

Student understood what happens when cold air meets warm air.

Score																				
total points																				
% equivalent																				

Activity Flip Chart (p. 12)
How can you tell that water is moving?

Scoring Criteria

Student followed instructions to complete this activity.

Student **observed** what happened inside of the bowl when food coloring was added.

Student **communicated** how the water in the bowl was like the water in the water cycle.

Student understood that water is always moving.

Student **observed** the green color moving and changing shape and position within the water.

Score																				
total points																				
% equivalent																				

Use the following activity scoring to assess students' performance

Scoring Key

| **4** correct, complete, detailed | **3** partially correct, complete, detailed | **2** partially correct, partially complete, lacks some detail | **1** incorrect or incomplete, needs assistance |

Directed Inquiry (p. 204)
Explore: Which fossils match the plants and animals?

Scoring Criteria

Student followed directions to complete this activity.

Student understood that a fossil is a part or a print of a plant that lived long ago.

Student correctly matched fossils to animals and plants.

Student cut out and glued puzzle pieces of fossils and organisms.

Student **communicated** how the student used clues to match the fossils to the plants and animals.

| **Score** | total points |
| | % equivalent |

Guided Inquiry (pp. 218–219)
Investigate: How can you make a model of a fossil?

Scoring Criteria

Student followed directions to complete this activity.

Student pressed a shell into clay to make a **model** of a fossil.

Student wrote ways in whixh the fossil and the shell are alike and different.

Student **observed** a model of a fossil, **inferred** what object was used to make the model, and explained how the inference was made.

Student told how fossils give clues about living things.

| **Score** | total points |
| | % equivalent |

Activity Book

© Pearson Education, Inc

Use the following activity scoring to assess students' performance

Scoring Key

4 correct, complete, detailed	**3** partially correct, complete, detailed	**2** partially correct, partially complete, lacks some detail	**1** incorrect or incomplete, needs assistance

Activity Flip Chart (p. 13)
How do paleontologists dig for fossils?

Scoring Criteria

Student followed instructions to complete this activity.

Student **observed** the fossils found during the dig.

Student **inferred** how this activity was a model of a real paleontologist dig.

Student **communicated** what was found during the dig by drawing pictures of the fossils.

Student **inferred** why it is important to dig carefully and slowly for fossils.

Score	
total points	
% equivalent	

Activity Flip Chart (p. 14)
How can you tell what made the tracks?

Scoring Criteria

Student followed instructions to complete this activity.

Student **interpreted data** by deciding what item made each type of track.

Student was able to correctly match some tracks with the items.

Student **communicated** which tracks were the most difficult to match to the correct items.

Student **inferred** why it is sometimes difficult to decide what kind of living thing made a fossil track.

Score	
total points	
% equivalent	

Scoring Key

| **4** correct, complete, detailed | **3** partially correct, complete, detailed | **2** partially correct, partially complete, lacks some detail | **1** incorrect or incomplete, needs assistance |

© Pearson Education, Inc.

Use the following activity scoring to assess students' performance

Full Inquiry (pp. 228–229)
Experiment: Does gravel, sand, or soil make the best imprint?

Scoring Criteria																									
Student made a **hypothesis** about the material in which the best impression of a shell is made.																									
Student tested the **hypothesis** by making an imprint of a shell in sand, potting soil, and gravel.																									
Student **collected** and recorded test **data** on a chart to show in which material the best imprint was made.																									
Student formed a conclusion about which material makes the best imprint.																									
Student made an **inference** about which material would make the best imprint.																									
Score	total points																								
	% equivalent																								

Activity Book

Use the following activity scoring to assess students' performance

Scoring Key

4 correct, complete, detailed	**3** partially correct, complete, detailed	**2** partially correct, partially complete, lacks some detail	**1** incorrect or incomplete, needs assistance

Directed Inquiry (p. 236)
Explore: What happens when oil is mixed with water?

Scoring Criteria

Student followed directions to complete this activity.

Student **measured** equal amounts of oil and water and mixed the liquids together.

Student **observed** the results of shaking oil and water in a jar.

Student reported that oil and water do not stay mixed together when shaken.

Student **inferred** that oil could be separated from water by allowing the mixture to stand until all the oil floats to the top.

Score	total points
	% equivalent

Guided Inquiry (pp. 256–257)
Investigate: How can water change?

Scoring Criteria

Student **observed** liquid and solid water.

Student **measured** the temperature of liquid water and solid water.

Student **predicted** what would happen to the temperature of the frozen water and what would happen to the outside of the cup.

Student compared the properties of liquid water to solid water.

Student **predicted** how long the liquid water would take to evaporate.

Score	total points
	% equivalent

Scoring Key

| **4** correct, complete, detailed | **3** partially correct, complete, detailed | **2** partially correct, partially complete, lacks some detail | **1** incorrect or incomplete, needs assistance |

Use the following activity scoring to assess students' performance

Activity Flip Chart (p. 15)
How are solids different from liquids?

Scoring Criteria

Student followed instructions to complete this activity.

Student **observed** each material.

Student **compared** how each material was alike and different.

Student **classified** each material by whether it was solid or liquid.

Student **communicated** how the solids were alike and how the liquids were alike.

Score	
	total points
	% equivalent

Activity Flip Chart (p. 16)
How can you make an ice cube melt faster?

Scoring Criteria

Student followed instructions to complete this activity.

Student **measured** the time it took to melt the ice cube.

Student **recorded** the time it took to melt the ice cube in the chart.

Student **communicated** what was done to make the ice cube melt faster.

Student **predicted** how to make the ice cubes melt even faster.

Score	
	total points
	% equivalent

Class Record Sheets

Use the following activity scoring to assess students' performance

Scoring Key			
4 correct, complete, detailed	**3** partially correct, complete, detailed	**2** partially correct, partially complete, lacks some detail	**1** incorrect or incomplete, needs assistance

Directed Inquiry (p. 268)
Explore: Which color heats faster?

Scoring Criteria

Student followed directions to complete this activity.																																			
Student placed in the Sun one thermometer wrapped in white paper and one thermometer wrapped in black paper.																																			
After one hour, student read the temperature wrapped in white paper.																																			
After one hour, student read the temperature wrapped in black paper.																																			
Student **inferred** that the color black raised the temperature faster.																																			

Score	
total points	
% equivalent	

Guided Inquiry (pp. 290–291)
Investigate: How can you change light?

Scoring Criteria

Student followed directions to complete this activity.																																			
Student **observed** the colors in the reflected light.																																			
Student drew what was **observed**.																																			
Student named some of the colors **observed** in the reflected light.																																			
Student **inferred** how light changes when it passes through water.																																			

Score	
total points	
% equivalent	

Use the following activity scoring to assess students' performance

Scoring Key

4 correct, complete, detailed	**3** partially correct, complete, detailed	**2** partially correct, partially complete, lacks some detail	**1** incorrect or incomplete, needs assistance

Activity Flip Chart (p. 17)
How does electricity make a light bulb light up?

Scoring Criteria

Student followed directions to complete this activity.

Student drew a picture of the closed circuit he/she made.

Student labeled the wires, battery, and light bulb in the drawing of the closed circuit.

Student **inferred** what would happen if only one wire touched the light bulb.

Student **communicated** what things he/she needed to make a closed circuit in this activity.

Score	total points
	% equivalent

Activity Flip Chart (p. 18)
What gives off heat?

Scoring Criteria

Student followed instructions to complete this activity.

Student **measured** the four temperatures using a thermometer.

Student recorded the temperature data in the chart.

Student **inferred** what things gave off heat in this activity.

Student **communicated** what happens to heat when the temperature on the thermometer goes down.

Score	total points
	% equivalent

Scoring Key

4 correct, complete, detailed	**3** partially correct, complete, detailed	**2** partially correct, partially complete, lacks some detail	**1** incorrect or incomplete, needs assistance

Use the following activity scoring to assess students' performance

Directed Inquiry (p. 300)
Explore: How can you measure force?

Scoring Criteria

Student followed directions to complete this activity.

Student **measured** the length of a rubber band as it pulled one book.

Student **measured** the length of the same rubber band as it pulled two books.

Student, when asked, explained that the rubber band stretched longer when more force is being used.

Student compared the two **measurements** of the rubber band.

Score	
total points	
% equivalent	

Directed Inquiry (pp. 322–323)
Investigate: What can magnets do?

Scoring Criteria

Student followed directions to complete this activity.

Student **observed** what happens when the north and south ends of two magnets are pushed together.

Student **observed** what happens when the north ends of two magnets are pushed together.

Student **predicted** and **observed** which objects a magnet will pull and reported his predictions and observations.

Student **observed** and recorded in a table, and reported if a magnet would pull a paper clip through air (gas), a plastic cup (solid), water (liquid), or paper (a solid).

Score	
total points	
% equivalent	

Activity Book

Class Record Sheet **T55**

Use the following activity scoring to assess students' performance

Scoring Key

| **4** correct, complete, detailed | **3** partially correct, complete, detailed | **2** partially correct, partially complete, lacks some detail | **1** incorrect or incomplete, needs assistance |

Activity Flip Chart (p. 19)
Do heavy objects fall faster than light objects?

Scoring Criteria

Student followed instructions to complete this activity.

Student **predicted** which object would fall faster.

Student recorded the data in the chart.

Student **communicated** whether the prediction was correct.

Student **communicated** how heavy and light objects fall.

Score																							
total points																							
% equivalent																							

Activity Flip Chart (p. 20)
How do objects move on different surfaces?

Scoring Criteria

Student followed instructions to complete this activity.

Student **observed** how the washer moved across each surface differently.

Student recorded how far the washer moved across each surface.

Student **interpreted data** by finding out why the washer moved different amounts on different surfaces.

Student understood that friction causes objects to slow down their movement.

Score																							
total points																							
% equivalent																							

Class Record Sheet

Scoring Key

| **4** correct, complete, detailed | **3** partially correct, complete, detailed | **2** partially correct, partially complete, lacks some detail | **1** incorrect or incomplete, needs assistance |

Use the following activity scoring to assess students' performance

Directed Inquiry (p. 332)
Explore: How can you make sound?

Scoring Criteria

Student followed directions to complete this activity

Student stayed on-task during the activity.

Student **observed** the sound made by pushing the free end of a ruler placed on a table.

Student **observed** the sound made when the free end of the ruler is shortened

Student **observed** and told how the sound changed when the length of the free end of the ruler changed.

Score	total points	% equivalent

Guided Inquiry (pp. 346–347)
Investigate: How can you change sound?

Scoring Criteria

Student followed directions to complete this activity.

Student **inferred** that plucking hard on a rubber band makes a loud sound and plucking gently makes a soft sound.

Student **predicted** how the length of the rubber band causes a change in pitch.

Student **inferred** that plucking a shorter rubber band makes a higher sound.

Student **inferred** that a soft (quiet), low pitch sound could be made by gently plucking the rubber band when the pencils were far apart.

Score	total points	% equivalent

Use the following activity scoring to assess students' performance

Scoring Key

| **4** correct, complete, detailed | **3** partially correct, complete, detailed | **2** partially correct, partially complete, lacks some detail | **1** incorrect or incomplete, needs assistance |

Activity Flip Chart (p. 21)
How can you describe sound?

Scoring Criteria

Student followed instructions to complete this activity.

Student **observed** the sounds each jar made.

Student **communicated** the pitch of each sound the jar made.

Student **communicated** how they changed the sound from each jar.

Student was able to describe sound.

| **Score** | total points | |
| | % equivalent | |

Activity Flip Chart (p. 22)
How does sound travel?

Scoring Criteria

Student followed instructions to complete this activity.

Student **observed** what happened in the water after putting the tuning fork into it.

Student recorded the observation in the chart.

Student **inferred** that the sound was traveling through the water by the ripples it was making in the water.

Student **inferred** that sound travels in small waves in the air.

| **Score** | total points | |
| | % equivalent | |

Class Record Sheet

Use the following activity scoring to assess students' performance

Scoring Key

4 correct, complete, detailed	**3** partially correct, complete, detailed	**2** partially correct, partially complete, lacks some detail	**1** incorrect or incomplete, needs assistance

Full Inquiry (pp. 356–357)

Experiment: What kinds of objects reflect light clearly?

Scoring Criteria

	Score	total points	% equivalent
Student followed directions to complete this activity.			
Student made a **hypothesis** about how well smooth and shiny objects reflect light.			
Student **classified** objects as smooth or not smooth and as shiny or not shiny.			
Student tested how clearly objects reflected light.			
Student concluded that smooth and shiny objects reflect light clearly and the student explained how he/she knew.			

Use the following activity scoring to assess students' performance

Scoring Key

| **4** correct, complete, detailed | **3** partially correct, complete, detailed | **2** partially correct, partially complete, lacks some detail | **1** incorrect or incomplete, needs assistance |

Directed Inquiry (p. 364)
Explore: What causes day and night?

Scoring Criteria

Student followed directions to complete this activity.

Student made a **model** of Earth.

Student used a flashlight to model the Sun.

Student **observed** the position and movement of the Sun and Earth in space using a flashlight for the Sun and the model for Earth.

Student explained how the model showed day and night.

Score	
total points	
% equivalent	

Guided Inquiry (pp. 384–385)
Investigate: How can you make a model of a constellation?

Scoring Criteria

Student made a **model** constellation.

Student **observed** how light shining through holes in paper can show the model constellation.

Student drew and named the **model** constellation.

Student told about the **model** constellation, and compared and contrasted it with a real constellation.

Student **made a definition** of a constellation.

Score	
total points	
% equivalent	

Scoring Key

| **4** correct, complete, detailed | **3** partially correct, complete, detailed | **2** partially correct, partially complete, lacks some detail | **1** incorrect or incomplete, needs assistance |

Use the following activity scoring to assess students' performance

Activity Flip Chart (p. 23)
What causes the seasons?

Scoring Criteria

Student followed instructions to complete this activity.

Student **made a model** of the Sun by laying a flashlight on a stack of books so that it was shining on the globe.

Student **inferred** where the Sun's position is in the beginning of winter.

Student **inferred** where the Sun's position is in the beginning summer.

Student understood what causes the seasons to change where he or she lives.

Score	
total points	
% equivalent	

Activity Flip Chart (p. 24)
What do constellations look like?

Scoring Criteria

Student followed instructions to complete this activity.

Student **made a model** of a constellation after understanding what one looks like.

Student **communicated** what other animal or object the constellation might look like if the dots were connected differently

Student understood that scientists make up names for constellations.

Student understood that the Big and Little Dippers are not complete constellations themselves, but are each part of the constellations Ursa Major (Big Bear) and Ursa Minor (Little Bear).

Score	
total points	
% equivalent	

© Pearson Education, Inc

Scoring Key			
4 correct, complete, detailed	**3** partially correct, complete, detailed	**2** partially correct, partially complete, lacks some detail	**1** incorrect or incomplete, needs assistance

Use the following activity scoring to assess students' performance

Directed Inquiry (p. 396)
Explore: How can you move the ball?

Scoring Criteria

Student followed directions to complete this activity.

Student stayed on-task during the activity.

Student did not touch the ball with his or her hands.

Student found a way to move the ball into the cup.

Student **communicated** how he or she solved the problem.

Score			
total points			
% equivalent			

Guided Inquiry (pp. 410–411)
Investigate: How can you make a maze?

Scoring Criteria

Student followed directions to complete this activity.

Student drew a plan for a maze and built a maze based on the plan.

Student **predicted** if a marble would follow in the maze.

Student tested, observed, and modified the maze.

Student **communicated** how the parts of the maze worked together.

Score			
total points			
% equivalent			

| Scoring Key | **4** correct, complete, detailed | **3** partially correct, complete, detailed | **2** partially correct, partially complete, lacks some detail | **1** incorrect or incomplete, needs assistance |

Use the following activity scoring to assess students' performance

Activity Flip Chart (p. 25)

How can you make a helicopter?

Scoring Criteria

Student followed instructions to complete this activity.

Student **observed** how each model helicopter fell.

Student **observed** how each model helicopter was different.

Student **communicated** how each model flew differently.

Student drew pictures of the model helicopters.

| Score | total points |
| | % equivalent |

Activity Flip Chart (p. 26)

How can you build a strong bridge?

Scoring Criteria

Student followed instructions to complete this activity.

Student **predicted** how much weight the bridge would hold.

Student **collected data** and recorded **observations** of how much weight the bridge would hold.

Student **communicated** what shapes the bridge was constructed out of.

Student **interpreted data** by **communicating** how the shape of the bridge affects how strong it is.

| Score | total points |
| | % equivalent |

Activity Rubric
Unit D

Use the following activity scoring to assess students' performance

Scoring Key

| **4** correct, complete, detailed | **3** partially correct, complete, detailed | **2** partially correct, partially complete, lacks some detail | **1** incorrect or incomplete, needs assistance |

Full Inquiry (pp. 420-421)
Experiment: Which tissue is the strongest?

Scoring Criteria

Scoring Criteria																			
Student followed directions to complete this activity.																			
Student made a **hypothesis** about the relation between the cost of a tissue and its strength.																			
Student tested his or her **hypothesis** by placing marbles on wet tissues and finding the total number of marbles each tissue held.																			
Student **collected** and recorded test **data** on a chart to show the number and mass of marbles each tissue could support.																			
Student formed a conclusion about which tissue was the strongest.																			
Score total points																			
Score % equivalent																			

Activity Rubric

Explore: Do plants need water?

Scoring Criteria	1	2	3	4
Student followed directions to complete activity.				
Student described what happened to celery without water for one day.				
Student **predicted** the result of adding water to wilted celery.				
Student described how and why wilted celery changed after placing it in water.				
Student **predicted** what will happen if the celery is taken out of the water.				

Scoring Key

4 points   correct, complete, detailed
3 points   partially correct, complete, detailed
2 points   partially correct, partially complete, lacks some detail
1 point   incorrect or incomplete, needs assistance.

Activity Rubric

Investigate: Do plants need light?

Scoring Criteria	1	2	3	4
Student followed directions to complete this activity.				
Student stayed on-task during this activity.				
Student **observed** both plants daily.				
Student recorded **observations** by filling in the chart with drawings.				
Student **inferred** that a plant will die if it does not get sunlight.				

Scoring Key

4 points correct, complete, detailed
3 points partially correct, complete, detailed
2 points partially correct, partially complete, lacks
 some detail
1 point incorrect or incomplete, needs assistance

Activity Rubric

Explore: How are worms and snakes alike and different?

Scoring Criteria	1	2	3	4
Student followed directions to complete this activity.				
Student **made a model** of a worm.				
Student **made a model** of a snake.				
Student felt the worm model and told how it felt.				
Student felt the snake model and told how it felt.				

Scoring Key
4 points correct, complete, detailed
3 points partially correct, complete, detailed
2 points partially correct, partially complete, lacks some detail
1 point incorrect or incomplete, needs assistance.

Name _____

Activity Rubric

Investigate: How can an octopus use its arms?

Scoring Criteria	1	2	3	4
Student followed directions to complete this activity.				
Student **predicted** the number of suction cups needed to open the jar.				
Student figured out how to place the suction cups.				
Student recorded the **prediction** and result in a bar graph.				
Student **communicated** how the suction cups were used.				

Scoring Key

4 points correct, complete, detailed
3 points partially correct, complete, detailed
2 points partially correct, partially complete, lacks some detail
1 point incorrect or incomplete, needs assistance.

Activity Rubric

Explore: What does yeast need to grow?

Scoring Criteria	1	2	3	4
Student followed directions to complete this activity.				
Student stayed on-task during the activity.				
Student **estimated** how long it took for bubbles to appear after water and sugar were added to yeast.				
Student **observed** the effect of mixing yeast, water, and sugar.				
Student **inferred** that yeast bubbles when it uses sugar and water as food.				

Scoring Key

4 points correct, complete, detailed
3 points partially correct, complete, detailed
2 points partially correct, partially complete, lacks some detail
1 point incorrect or incomplete, needs assistance

Activity Rubric

Investigate: How can you model a food web?

Scoring Criteria	1	2	3	4
Student followed directions to complete activity.				
Student tossed a ball to another student.				
Student drew the **model** of the food web and recorded the organisms' names.				
Student **inferred** what the food web lines represented.				
Student explained how the food web **model** represents a real life food web.				

Scoring Key

4 points   correct, complete, detailed
3 points   partially correct, complete, detailed
2 points   partially correct, partially complete, lacks some detail
1 point   incorrect or incomplete, needs assistance

Activity Rubric

Explore: Which hand do different children use to write?

Scoring Criteria	1	2	3	4
Student followed directions to complete this activity.				
Student stayed on-task during the activity.				
Student identified the hand with which the student writes.				
Student taped a hand cutout correctly on the graph.				
Student **inferred** that some people are left-handed and some are right-handed from data on graph.				

Scoring Key

4 points correct, complete, detailed
3 points partially correct, complete, detailed
2 points partially correct, partially complete, lacks some detail
1 point incorrect or incomplete, needs assistance.

Activity Rubric

Investigate: How does a caterpillar grow and change?

Scoring Criteria	1	2	3	4
Student **observed** a butterfly's life cycle every day for three weeks.				
Student **collected data** every day for three weeks.				
Student **predicted** that a butterfly would emerge from the chrysalis.				
Student drew pictures to show the stages of a butterfly's development and described how it changed.				
Student **inferred** that the butterfly developed inside the chrysalis.				

Scoring Key

4 points   correct, complete, detailed
3 points   partially correct, complete, detailed
2 points   partially correct, partially complete, lacks some detail
1 point   incorrect or incomplete, needs assistance.

Name _____

Activity Rubrics

Experiment: Which bird beak can crush seeds?

Scoring Criteria	1	2	3	4
Student made a **hypothesis** about the type of bird beak that can crush seeds.				
Student tested the hypothesis by **making and using models** of a heron's beak and a cardinal's beak.				
Student **collected** and recorded **data** that showed the results of testing the bird beak **models.**				
Students told which **model** crushes a piece of straw.				
Student **inferred** which bird beak can crush seeds.				

Scoring Key

4 points correct, complete, detailed
3 points partially correct, complete, detailed
2 points partially correct, partially complete, lacks some detail
1 point incorrect or incomplete, needs assistance

Activity Rubric

Explore: How are soils different?

Scoring Criteria	1	2	3	4
Student followed directions to complete this activity.				
Student **observed** the appearance, smell, and texture of sandy soil and potting soil.				
Student **observed** the absorptive qualities of sandy soil and potting soil.				
Student described how sandy soil and potting soil are alike.				
Student described how sandy soil and potting soil are different.				

Scoring Key

4 points correct, complete, detailed
3 points partially correct, complete, detailed
2 points partially correct, partially complete, lacks some detail
1 point incorrect or incomplete, needs assistance.

Activity Rubric

Investigate: How do worms change the soil?

Scoring Criteria	1	2	3	4
Student followed directions to complete this activity.				
Student **observed** the compost bags for three weeks.				
Student **collected data** by making drawings in chart for three weeks.				
Student **inferred** that worms "ate" the leaves and incorporated the leaves into the soil.				
Student reported that the bag without worms had more leaves after three weeks.				

Scoring Key

4 points correct, complete, detailed
3 points partially correct, complete, detailed
2 points partially correct, partially complete, lacks some detail
1 point incorrect or incomplete, needs assistance

Name _____

Activity Rubric

Explore: How much rain falls?

Scoring Criteria	1	2	3	4
Student followed directions to complete this activity.				
Student stayed on-task during the activity.				
Student marked 12 lines 1 centimeter apart on a strip of masking tape.				
Student numbered the lines from 1 to 12.				
Student **inferred** how the rain gauge could be used to measure rainfall.				

Scoring Key

4 points correct, complete, detailed
3 points partially correct, complete, detailed
2 points partially correct, partially complete, lacks some detail
1 point incorrect or incomplete, needs assistance

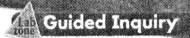
Activity Rubric

Investigate: How can you measure weather changes?

Scoring Criteria	1	2	3	4
Student checked the rain gauge and thermometer for one week.				
Student **collected data** on a chart to show daily rainfall and temperatures for one week.				
Student summarized the weather for the week.				
Student **classified** each day as rainy or not rainy.				
Student **interpreted data** by telling weather changes from day to day.				

Scoring Key

4 points correct, complete, detailed
3 points partially correct, complete, detailed
2 points partially correct, partially complete, lacks some detail
1 point incorrect or incomplete, needs assistance

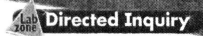
Activity Rubric

Explore: Which fossils match the plants and animals?

Scoring Criteria	1	2	3	4
Student followed directions to complete this activity.				
Student understood that a fossil is a part or a print of a plant that lived long ago.				
Student correctly matched fossils to animals and plants.				
Student cut out and glued puzzle pieces of fossils and organisms.				
Student **communicated** how the student used clues to match the fossils to the plants and animals.				

Scoring Key

4 points correct, complete, detailed
3 points partially correct, complete, detailed
2 points partially correct, partially complete, lacks some detail
1 point incorrect or incomplete, needs assistance

© Pearson Education, Inc

Activity Rubric

Investigate: How can you make a model of a fossil?

Scoring Criteria	1	2	3	4
Student followed directions to complete this activity.				
Student pressed a shell into clay to **make a model** of a fossil.				
Student wrote ways in which the fossil and the shell are alike and different.				
Student **observed** a model of a fossil, **inferred** what object was used to make the model, and explained how the inference was made.				
Student told how fossils give clues about living things.				

Scoring Key
4 points correct, complete, detailed
3 points partially correct, complete, detailed
2 points partially correct, partially complete, lacks some detail
1 point incorrect or incomplete, needs assistance

Name _____

Activity Rubric

Experiment: Does gravel, sand, or soil make the best imprint?

Scoring Criteria	1	2	3	4
Student made a **hypothesis** about the material in which the best impression of a shell is made.				
Student tested the **hypothesis** by making an imprint of a shell in sand, potting soil, and gravel.				
Student **collected** and recorded test **data** on a chart to show in which material the best imprint was made.				
Student formed a conclusion about which material makes the best imprint.				
Student made an **inference** about which material would make the best imprint.				

Scoring Key

4 points correct, complete, detailed
3 points partially correct, complete, detailed
2 points partially correct, partially complete, lacks some detail
1 point incorrect or incomplete, needs assistance

Activity Rubric

Explore: What happens when oil is mixed with water?

Scoring Criteria	1	2	3	4
Student followed directions to complete this activity.				
Student **measured** equal amounts of oil and water and mixed the liquids together.				
Student **observed** the results of shaking oil and water in a jar.				
Student reported that oil and water do not stay mixed together when shaken.				
Student **inferred** that oil could be separated from water by allowing the mixture to stand until all the oil floats to the top, at which time the oil could be poured out.				

Scoring Key

4 points correct, complete, detailed
3 points partially correct, complete, detailed
2 points partially correct, partially complete, lacks some detail
1 point incorrect or incomplete, needs assistance

Name _____

Activity Rubric

Investigate: How can water change?

Scoring Criteria	1	2	3	4
Student **observed** liquid and solid water.				
Student **measured** the temperature of liquid water and solid water.				
Student **predicted** what would happen to the temperature of the frozen water and what would happen to the outside of the cup.				
Student compared the properties of liquid water to solid water.				
Student **predicted** how long the liquid water would take to evaporate.				

Scoring Key

4 points correct, complete, detailed
3 points partially correct, complete, detailed
2 points partially correct, partially complete, lacks some detail
1 point   incorrect or incomplete, needs assistance

Activity Rubric

Explore: Which color heats faster?

Scoring Criteria	1	2	3	4
Student followed directions to complete this activity.				
Student placed in the Sun one thermometer wrapped in white paper and one thermometer wrapped in black paper.				
After one hour, student read the temperature wrapped in white paper.				
After one hour, student read the temperature wrapped in black paper.				
Student **inferred** that the color black raised the temperature faster.				

Scoring Key

4 points   correct, complete, detailed
3 points   partially correct, complete, detailed
2 points   partially correct, partially complete, lacks some detail
1 point   incorrect or incomplete, needs assistance

Activity Rubric

Investigate: How can you change light?

Scoring Criteria	1	2	3	4
Student followed directions to complete this activity.				
Student **observed** the colors in the reflected light.				
Student drew what was **observed.**				
Student named some of the colors **observed** in the reflected light.				
Student **inferred** how light changes when it passes though water.				

Scoring Key

4 points correct, complete, detailed
3 points partially correct, complete, detailed
2 points partially correct, partially complete, lacks some detail
1 point incorrect or incomplete, needs assistance

Activity Rubric

Explore: How can you measure force?

Scoring Criteria	1	2	3	4
Student followed directions to complete this activity.				
Student **measured** the length of a rubber band as it pulled one book.				
Student **measured** the length of the same rubber band as it pulled two books.				
Student, when asked, explained that the rubber band stretched longer when more force is being used.				
Student compared the two **measurements** of the rubber band.				

Scoring Key
4 points correct, complete, detailed
3 points partially correct, complete, detailed
2 points partially correct, partially complete, lacks some detail
1 point incorrect or incomplete, needs assistance

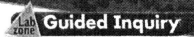
Activity Rubric

Investigate: What can magnets do?

Scoring Criteria	1	2	3	4
Student followed directions to complete this activity.				
Student **observed** what happens when the north and south ends of two magnets are pushed together.				
Student **observed** what happens when the north ends of two magnets are pushed together.				
Student **predicted** and **observed** which objects a magnet will pull and reported his predictions and observations.				
Student **observed** and recorded in a table, and reported if a magnet would pull a paper clip through air (gas), a plastic cup (solid), water (liquid), or paper (a solid).				

Scoring Key

4 points correct, complete, detailed
3 points partially correct, complete, detailed
2 points partially correct, partially complete, lacks some detail
1 point incorrect or incomplete, needs assistance

Activity Rubric

Explore: How can you make sound?

Scoring Criteria	1	2	3	4
Student followed directions to complete this activity.				
Student stayed on-task during the activity.				
Student **observed** the sound made by pushing the free end of a ruler placed on a table.				
Student **observed** the sound made when the free end of the ruler is shortened.				
Student **observed** and told how the sound changed when the length of the free end of the ruler changed.				

Scoring Key

4 points correct, complete, detailed
3 points partially correct, complete, detailed
2 points partially correct, partially complete, lacks some detail
1 point incorrect or incomplete, needs assistance

© Pearson Education, Inc

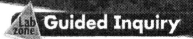

Activity Rubric

Investigate: How can you change sound?

Scoring Criteria	1	2	3	4
Student followed directions to complete this activity.				
Student **inferred** that plucking hard on a rubber band makes a loud sound and plucking gently makes a soft sound.				
Student **predicted** how the length of the rubber band causes a change in pitch.				
Student **inferred** that plucking a shorter rubber band makes a higher sound.				
Student **inferred** that a soft (quiet), low pitch sound could be made by gently plucking the rubber band when the pencils were far apart.				

Scoring Key

4 points correct, complete, detailed
3 points partially correct, complete, detailed
2 points partially correct, partially complete, lacks some detail
1 point incorrect or incomplete, needs assistance

Activity Rubric

Experiment: What kinds of objects reflect light clearly?

Scoring Criteria	1	2	3	4
Student followed directions to complete this activity.				
Student made a hypothesis about how well smooth and shiny objects reflect light.				
Student classified objects as smooth or not smooth and as shiny or not shiny.				
Student tested how clearly objects reflected light.				
Student concluded that smooth and shiny objects reflect light clearly and the student explained how he/she knew.				

Scoring Key

4 points correct, complete, detailed
3 points partially correct, complete, detailed
2 points partially correct, partially complete, lacks
           some detail
1 point incorrect or incomplete, needs assistance

Activity Rubric

Explore: What causes night and day?

Scoring Criteria	1	2	3	4
Student followed directions to complete this activity.				
Student made a **model** of Earth.				
Student used a flashlight to model the Sun.				
Student **observed** the position and movement of the Sun and Earth in space using a flashlight for the Sun and the model for Earth.				
Student explained how the model showed day and night.				

Scoring Key

4 points correct, complete, detailed
3 points partially correct, complete, detailed
2 points partially correct, partially complete, lacks some detail
1 point incorrect or incomplete, needs assistance

Activity Rubric

Investigate: How can you make a model of a constellation?

Scoring Criteria	1	2	3	4
Student made a **model** constellation.				
Student **observed** how light shining through holes in paper can show the model constellation.				
Student drew and named the **model** constellation.				
Student told about the **model** constellation, and compared and contrasted it with a real constellation.				
Student **made a definition** of a constellation.				

Scoring Key

4 points correct, complete, detailed
3 points partially correct, complete, detailed
2 points partially correct, partially complete, lacks some detail
1 point incorrect or incomplete, needs assistance

© Pearson Education, Inc

Name _____

Activity Rubric

Explore: How can you move the ball?

Scoring Criteria	1	2	3	4
Student followed directions to complete this activity.				
Student stayed on-task during the activity.				
Student did not touch the ball with his or her hands.				
Student found a way to move the ball into the cup.				
Student **communicated** how he or she solved the problem.				

Scoring Key

4 points   correct, complete, detailed
3 points   partially correct, complete, detailed
2 points   partially correct, partially complete, lacks
               some detail
1 point   incorrect or incomplete, needs assistance

Activity Rubric

Investigate: How can you make a maze?

Scoring Criteria	1	2	3	4
Student followed directions to complete this activity.				
Student drew a plan for a maze and built a maze based on the plan.				
Student **predicted** if a marble would follow in the maze.				
Student tested, observed, and modified the maze.				
Student **communicated** how the parts of the maze worked together.				

Scoring Key

4 points correct, complete, detailed
3 points partially correct, complete, detailed
2 points partially correct, partially complete, lacks some detail
1 point incorrect or incomplete, needs assistance

Name _____

Activity Rubric

Experiment: Which tissue is the strongest?

Scoring Criteria	1	2	3	4
Student followed directions to complete this activity.				
Student made a **hypothesis** about the relation between the cost of a tissue and its strength.				
Student tested his or her **hypothesis** by placing marbles on wet tissues and finding the total number of marbles each tissue held.				
Student **collected** and recorded test **data** on a chart to show the number and mass of marbles each tissue could support.				
Student formed a conclusion about which tissue was the strongest.				

Scoring Key

4 points   correct, complete, detailed
3 points   partially correct, complete, detailed
2 points   partially correct, partially complete, lacks some detail
1 point   incorrect or incomplete, needs assistance

© Pearson Education, Inc

Name _____

Practice Observing

To **observe** means to use any of your five senses to find out about objects or things that happen

You can practice observing by seeing, tasting, smelling, listening to, or touching objects.

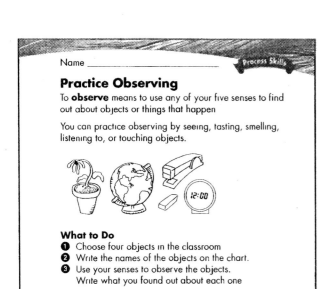

What to Do
❶ Choose four objects in the classroom
❷ Write the names of the objects on the chart.
❸ Use your senses to observe the objects. Write what you found out about each one

Things I Observe	
Object	**How It Looks, Sounds, Smells, Feels**
a globe	It is round and smooth.

Activity Book   Process Skill Activity **1**

Name _____

Explain Your Results
1. Write the name of an object you observed using more than one sense. Write the senses you used to observe that object.
Answers will vary, but should include one object that could be observed with more than one sense and name the senses used.

2. Which of your five senses did you use most often?
Students will probably list the sense of sight.

2 Process Skill Activity   Activity Book

Name _____

Practice Communicating

To **communicate** means to share what you learn. You can use words, pictures, charts, diagrams, or graphs.

Talking with your partner is communicating You can practice communicating by describing animals.

What to Do
❶ Think of an animal.
❷ Give clues to a partner. Tell how the animal moves and looks. Describe what it does.
❸ Record each clue in the chart until your partner guesses the animal.

Animal	Clues
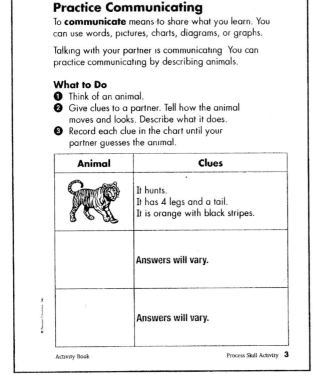	It hunts. It has 4 legs and a tail. It is orange with black stripes.
	Answers will vary.
	Answers will vary.

Activity Book   Process Skill Activity **3**

Name _____

Explain Your Results
1. How many clues did you give?
Answers will vary, but should be the same as the number of clues listed in the chart.
2. Which clues helped your partner the most? Why?
Answers will vary, but should indicate the most descriptive clues that were specific to that animal.

4 Process Skill Activity   Activity Book

Practice Estimating and Measuring

Estimate and measure means to tell what you think an object's measure is. Then you measure it and tell the amount or size.

You can practice by estimating and measuring the height of your desk.

Materials
metric ruler or meter stick

What to Do
❶ Make an estimate How many centimeters is it from the top to the bottom of your desk?
❷ Write down your estimate
❸ Use a metric ruler or meter stick to measure the number of centimeters
❹ Write down the number of centimeters

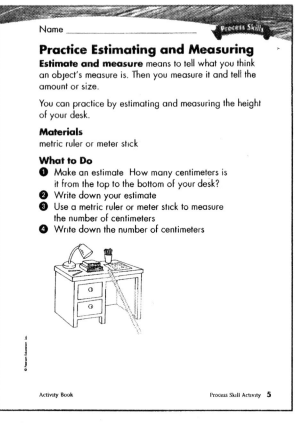

Explain Your Results
1. What was the difference between your estimate and your measurement?
Answers will vary. Children should find the difference by subtracting.
2. What helped you to make a good estimate?
Answers will vary, but should indicate knowledge that a centimeter is a small measurement so the estimate would be a fairly large number.

Practice Collecting Data

Recording what you observe and measure is **collecting data.** You can record data in a table, chart, graph, or diagram.

You can practice collecting data. Make a chart that shows your height and a partner's height.

Materials
metric tape measure
masking tape

What to Do
❶ Tape a tape measure to a wall Tape the "zero" end at the bottom of the wall. Tape the end with high numbers as high as it will go
❷ Stand next to the tape measure Put your back to the wall
❸ Have your partner write your height in the chart.
❹ Switch roles. Write your partner's height in the chart.

Name	Height

Explain Your Results
1. What would you do if you had the height of every student in the room? How would you change the chart?
The chart would have to have more rows.

2. How could you record the same data using words or pictures instead of a chart?
Answers will vary. Sample answer: Draw a picture of a tape measure and write each child's name beside the number that shows his or her height.

Practice Classifying

You **classify** when you group objects by how they are alike.

You classify when you think about how some animals are alike. Practice classifying by sorting animal cards

Materials
index cards
crayons

What to Do
❶ Take 9 cards and draw one animal on each card. Draw 3 kinds of fish, 3 four-legged mammals, and 3 types of birds on the cards.
❷ Mix up the cards and give them to a partner
❸ Look at the cards your partner gave you Classify the cards into 3 groups.
❹ Talk with your partner about how you sorted the cards.

Explain Your Results
1. How did you and your partner classify the animals on the cards?
Children should say that the animals were classified as follows: fish, birds, and mammals (or animals with four legs).
2. Name ways that the animals in each group are alike.
possible answers: the fish swim, live in water, and have scales; the birds fly and have feathers; the mammals have hair and four legs.

Practice Inferring

Infer means to draw conclusions from what you observe or know.

You infer when you look at a picture and get an idea about what is happening Practice inferring as you talk about pictures with a partner. Use this information:

In many places, trees grow leaves and flowers in the spring. All summer the trees have green leaves. In fall the leaves turn yellow, orange, and red. Then the leaves fall off. The trees have no leaves in winter.

Materials
paper
crayons

What to Do
❶ Choose a season. Draw a color picture of a tree in that season.
❷ Show your picture to a partner Have your partner infer the season. Look at the picture your partner drew. Infer the season in your partner's picture.
❸ Talk with your partner about your pictures Talk about how you inferred what season each picture showed.
❹ Look at the pictures in the chart. Infer the seasons Fill in the chart.

Picture	Season
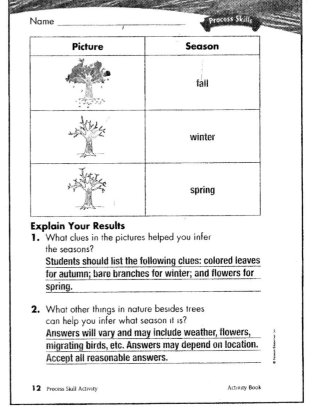	fall
	winter
	spring

Explain Your Results
1. What clues in the pictures helped you infer the seasons?
Students should list the following clues: colored leaves for autumn; bare branches for winter; and flowers for spring.

2. What other things in nature besides trees can help you infer what season it is?
Answers will vary and may include weather, flowers, migrating birds, etc. Answers may depend on location. Accept all reasonable answers.

Practice Predicting

Predicting is telling what you think might happen

Practice predicting by telling what will happen when you mix two colors together.

Materials
red paint
yellow paint
blue paint
brushes or sticks
paper plate

What to Do
❶ Read the chart. Predict the colors you will get.
❷ Write the color names in the chart.
❸ Then mix the colors.
❹ What happened? What color did you make?
Write the colors in the chart.

Colors to Mix	Color I Predict	Color I Made
red + yellow =	Answer will vary.	orange
red + blue =	Answer will vary.	purple
blue + yellow =	Answer will vary.	green

Explain Your Results

1. How many colors did you predict correctly?
Answers will vary.

2. What helped you to predict the colors you would make?
Possible answers: I mixed colors together in art class. I learned about colors when I painted in first grade.

Practice Making and Using Models

Making a model is making something to show what it is like or how it works

You can make and use models to show how animals are different Practice by making and using models of a spider and an insect.

Materials
pictures
14 pipe cleaners
clay

What to Do
❶ Look at the pictures of the spider and the insect.
❷ Count the body parts and legs of each.
❸ Use clay and pipe cleaners to make a model of each.
❹ Use the models to show a partner how the spider and the insect are different.

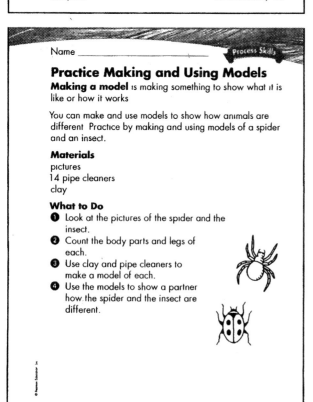

Explain Your Results

1. How did you use the pictures to help you make your models?
Answers will vary, but should indicate that the models were based on the animals in the pictures.

2. How are your models of a spider and an insect different?
The spider model has two body parts and eight legs. The insect model has three body parts and six legs.

Practice Interpreting Data

To **interpret data** means to use information you collected to solve a problem or answer a question.

Reading and thinking about information on a chart is interpreting data.

You can practice interpreting information on a weather chart.

What to Do

❶ Look at the information on the chart

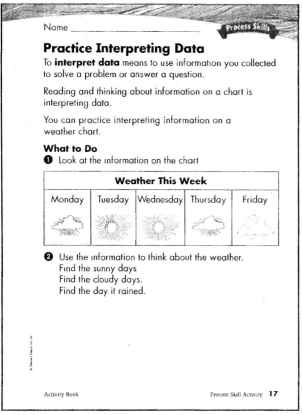

Weather This Week				
Monday	Tuesday	Wednesday	Thursday	Friday

❷ Use the information to think about the weather.
Find the sunny days
Find the cloudy days.
Find the day it rained.

Explain Your Results

1. Which days were sunny?
   Tuesday and Wednesday

2. What days were cloudy?
   Monday and Thursday

3. Which day did it rain?
   Friday

Practice Making Hypotheses

To **make a hypothesis** means to make a statement you can test to solve a problem or answer a question.

You can practice making a hypothesis by answering this question: Does a wet towel dry faster in a sunny, warm place or a dark, cool place?

Materials
2 paper towels
water

What to Do
❶ Do wet towels dry faster where it is sunny and warm or where it is dark and cool?
❷ Wet each towel in a tray filled with water
❸ Put one wet towel somewhere sunny and warm. Put the other wet towel somewhere dark and cool
❹ Test your hypothesis See which towel dries first.

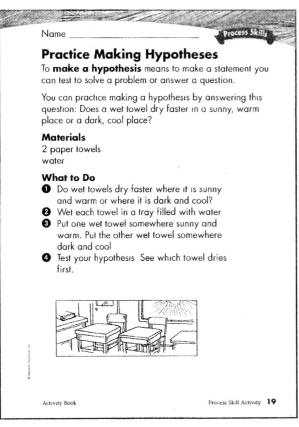

Explain Your Results

1. What was your hypothesis?
   Answer will most likely be: A wet towel in a sunny, warm place will dry out faster than a wet towel in a dark, cool place.

2. How did you test your hypothesis?
   Answer should include that one towel was placed in a sunny and warm spot and one towel was placed in a dark and cold place.

3. Was your hypothesis correct?
   Answers will vary.

Activity Book   Process Skills Answer Key **T99**

Practice Controlling Variables

To **control variables** means to change one thing that may affect what happens. Keep everything else the same

You can practice controlling variables by doing an experiment with water, cups, and objects of different sizes. You will experiment to see which object makes water rise the highest

Materials
3 objects of different sizes
3 cups
water
ruler

What to Do
❶ Take three cups that are the same size and shape.
❷ Pour the same amount of water in each cup
❸ Find a small, a medium, and a large object that will fit in a cup. Write or draw them in the chart.
❹ Put an object in each cup.
❺ Measure how much the water rises. Finish filling in the chart

---

Object	Water Level
paper clip	
eraser	
glue	

Explain Your Results
1. What did you find out in your experiment?
   Sample answer: Bigger objects made the water go up more.

2. What variable did you change?
   I changed the size of the objects.

3. What did you keep the same?
   I kept the amount of water the same.

Practice Making Definitions

Making a definition means using what you know now to describe something or tell what it means.

Practice making definitions by describing seeds, soil, water, and sunlight

Materials
seed
soil
water
pot

What to Do
❶ Plant your seed and water it Put it in a sunny place.
❷ Make definitions by filling in this chart.

Things that help a plant grow	What is it like?	How does it help a plant grow?
seed	small and hard	grows into a plant
soil	brown dirt	covers up the seed
water	liquid	keeps the seed wet
sunlight	bright and warm	keeps the plant warm and makes the plant grow

---

Explain Your Results
Write a definition for a seed, soil, water, and sunlight Write how each helps a plant grow. Use your chart to help you

1. What is a seed?
   Possible answer: A seed is a small hard thing that becomes a plant.

2. What is soil?
   Possible answer: Soil is brown dirt that covers the seed.

3. What is water?
   Possible answer: Water is a liquid that keeps a seed wet.

4. What is sunlight?
   Possible answer: Sunlight is light from the Sun that keeps a plant warm.

Practice Investigating and Experimenting

To **investigate and experiment** means to plan and do things to test a hypothesis or solve a problem. Then form a conclusion

You can practice investigating and experimenting by trying to answer the question, "Does sugar dissolve faster in warm or cold water?"

Materials
2 plastic cups
sugar
teaspoon

What to Do
❶ Fill one cup with warm water.
❷ Fill the other cup with cold water. Fill both cups with the same amount.
❸ Add 1 teaspoon of sugar to each cup. Stir
❹ Observe what happens to the sugar in each cup
❺ Record your results in the chart. Describe what you observe.

Cup with Warm Water	Cup with Cold Water
The sugar dissolved in the water.	There is some sugar on the bottom of the cup.

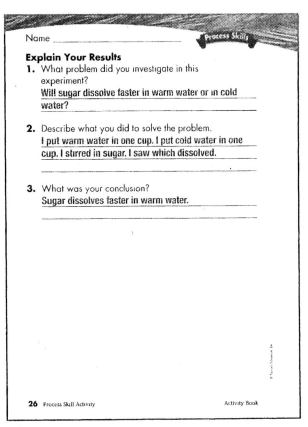

Explain Your Results

1. What problem did you investigate in this experiment?
   Will sugar dissolve faster in warm water or in cold water?

2. Describe what you did to solve the problem.
   I put warm water in one cup. I put cold water in one cup. I stirred in sugar. I saw which dissolved.

3. What was your conclusion?
   Sugar dissolves faster in warm water.

Explore Do plants need water?

❷ How did the celery change after one day in the jar?
The celery got droopy.

❸ What did you predict would happen when you put water in the jar?
Answers will vary but may include that the celery's leaves will look full again and the stalk will be crisp.

❹ How did the celery change after one day? Why did the celery change?
The celery looked crisp and fresh again. The water went up into the celery and that made it stiff and fresh.

Explain Your Results
Predict What will happen if you take the celery out of the water?
The celery will get droopy again.

Notes for Home: Your child learned how plants need water by observing what happens when a wilted stalk of celery is placed in a jar of water.
Home Activity: Discuss what happens to plants when it does not rain for a long time. Then discuss what happens to the plants when it rains. How is this like the celery activity he or she completed?

Investigate Do plants need light?

❹—❺ Fill in the chart. Draw pictures to show the plants each day

	Sunlight	Dark
Day 1		
Day 2		
Day 3		
Day 4		
Day 5		

Explain Your Results

1. Which plant grew better?
The plant in the light.

2. **Infer** What will happen if a plant does not get light?
The plant will not grow. It will die.

Go Further
What will happen if you move the plant from the dark place to a sunny place? Try it and find out
Answers will vary but may include: The plant may get green again if it did not die.

Notes for Home: Your child learned how plants need sunlight to grow by observing the effects of putting a plant in the sunlight for a week and putting a plant in the dark for one week.
Home Activity: Try this planting activity at home. Plant pea or bean seeds in two cups. Place one in the light and one in the dark. Observe the results.

Name _____

What are the parts of a flowering plant?

Explain Your Results

1. Make and Use Models: What are the main parts of a flowering plant?
roots, a stem, leaves, and flower

2. How does each part help the plant?
The leaf makes food for the plant. The flower makes seeds. The root takes in water and holds the plant in the ground. The stem holds the plant up and brings water up from the roots.

Notes for Home: Your child made a model of a flowering plant, labeled its parts, and communicated how each part helps the plant
Home Activity: With your child, find a flowering plant Discuss its parts and the function of each

---

Name _____

How are a cactus and a fern alike and different?

Explain Your Results
Observe In the chart below, record how the cactus and fern are alike and different.

	Alike	**Different**
Cactus	has roots, stems, and leaves	Cactuses have thick stems and sharp leaves that are spines.
Fern	has roots, stems, and leaves	Ferns have thin stems and wide leaves divided into many parts.

Notes for Home: Your child observed a cactus and a fern with a hand lens and communicated how the two plants are alike and different.
Home Activity: With your child, compare two types of plants and discuss how they are alike and different

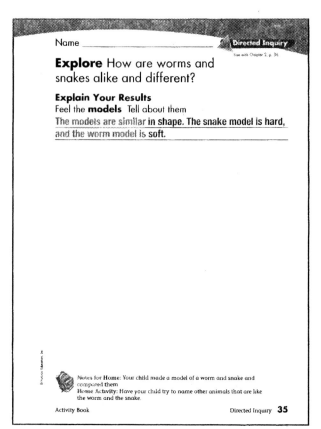

Explore How are worms and snakes alike and different?

Explain Your Results
Feel the **models** Tell about them
The models are similar in shape. The snake model is hard, and the worm model is soft.

Notes for Home: Your child made a model of a worm and snake and compared them
Home Activity: Have your child try to name other animals that are like the worm and the snake.

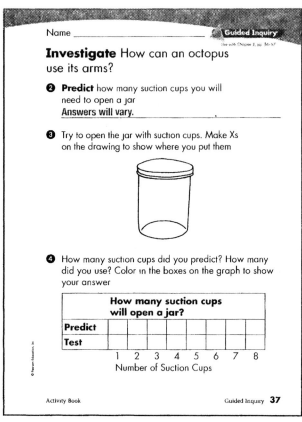

Investigate How can an octopus use its arms?

❷ **Predict** how many suction cups you will need to open a jar
Answers will vary.

❸ Try to open the jar with suction cups. Make Xs on the drawing to show where you put them

❹ How many suction cups did you predict? How many did you use? Color in the boxes on the graph to show your answer

How many suction cups will open a jar?								
Predict								
Test								

1 2 3 4 5 6 7 8
Number of Suction Cups

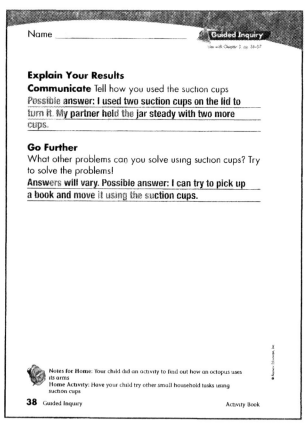

Explain Your Results
Communicate Tell how you used the suction cups
Possible answer: I used two suction cups on the lid to turn it. My partner held the jar steady with two more cups.

Go Further
What other problems can you solve using suction cups? Try to solve the problems!
Answers will vary. Possible answer: I can try to pick up a book and move it using the suction cups.

Notes for Home: Your child did an activity to find out how an octopus uses its arms
Home Activity: Have your child try other small household tasks using suction cups

Name _____

How does camouflage help an animal survive?

Explain Your Results

1. What helps your animal hide?
   Camouflage helps my animal hide.

2. **Infer** How does camouflage help your animal survive?
   It helps hide the animal so that it is hard for other animals to see it.

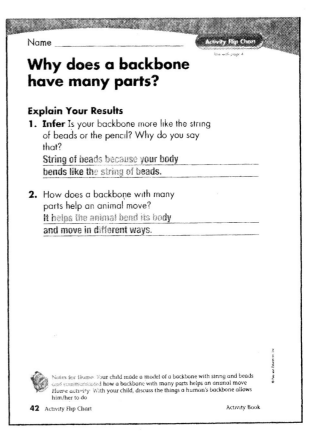

Notes for Home: Your child designed a habitat for an animal and inferred how camouflage helps an animal to survive in its habitat.
Home Activity: With your child, think of an animal that uses camouflage to help it survive Discuss how the camouflage protects the animal in its habitat

Activity Book   Activity Flip Chart **41**

Name _____

Why does a backbone have many parts?

Explain Your Results

1. **Infer** Is your backbone more like the string of beads or the pencil? Why do you say that?
   String of beads because your body bends like the string of beads.

2. How does a backbone with many parts help an animal move?
   It helps the animal bend its body and move in different ways.

Notes for Home: Your child made a model of a backbone with string and beads and communicated how a backbone with many parts helps an animal move
Home Activity: With your child, discuss the things a human's backbone allows him/her to do

42 Activity Flip Chart   Activity Book

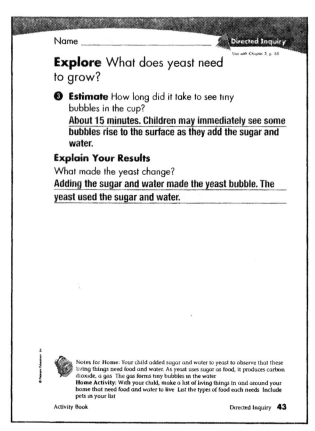

Explore What does yeast need
to grow?

❸ **Estimate** How long did it take to see tiny
bubbles in the cup?
**About 15 minutes. Children may immediately see some
bubbles rise to the surface as they add the sugar and
water.**

Explain Your Results
What made the yeast change?
**Adding the sugar and water made the yeast bubble. The
yeast used the sugar and water.**

Notes for Home: Your child added sugar and water to yeast to observe that these
living things need food and water. As yeast uses sugar as food, it produces carbon
dioxide, a gas. The gas forms tiny bubbles in the water
Home Activity: With your child, make a list of living things in and around your
home that need food and water to live. List the types of food each needs. Include
pets in your list

Investigate How can you
model a food web?

❹ Draw your food web. Write the names of all
the living things.

My Food Web

**Answers will vary, but web should
show correct relationships between
organisms. All organisms should be
labeled.**

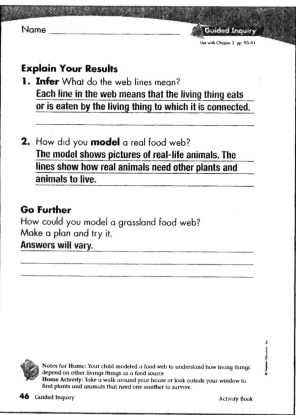

Explain Your Results
1. Infer What do the web lines mean?
**Each line in the web means that the living thing eats
or is eaten by the living thing to which it is connected.**

2. How did you **model** a real food web?
**The model shows pictures of real-life animals. The
lines show how real animals need other plants and
animals to live.**

Go Further
How could you model a grassland food web?
Make a plan and try it.
Answers will vary.

Notes for Home: Your child modeled a food web to understand how living things
depend on other livings things as a food source
Home Activity: Take a walk around your house or look outside your window to
find plants and animals that need one another to survive.

What is a food chain?

Explain Your Results
Make Definitions What does your food chain show?
The food chain shows how food passes
from the leaf to the owl.

© Pearson Education, Inc

Notes for Home: Your child made a food chain using pictures of a leaf, an insect, a small bird, and an owl
Home Activity: With your child, illustrate another food chain using crayons and drawing paper

How does a bird make a nest?

In the box below, draw a picture of the bird nest you made

Explain Your Results
1. **Classify** What plant parts does a bird use to make a nest?
   leaves, sticks, bark, grass

2. What animal parts does a bird use to make a nest?
   feathers

3. **Infer** how a nest helps birds
   A nest protects birds from predators, shelters it from
   weather, and keeps it and its eggs warm.

© Pearson Education, Inc

Notes for Home: Your child made a model of a bird nest and inferred how a nest helps birds
Home Activity: With your child, discuss how nests help other animals and the things those animals use to build nests

Explore Which hand do different children use to write?

Explain Your Results

Infer What does the graph show?

The graph shows that [number] children use their right hand to write and [number] use their left hand.

Notes for Home: Your child collected data that showed some children in the class are left-handed and others are right-handed. Your child learned one way in which people are different.
Home Activity: Observe differences in family members such as facial features, hair, or eye color.

Activity Book   Directed Inquiry **51**

Investigate How does a caterpillar grow and change?

❶ Use this chart to **collect data** on your caterpillars for 3 weeks.

	Observations
Week 1	
Monday	The notes in students' charts will vary, but
Tuesday	generally the larvae (caterpillar) will
Wednesday	develop into a chrysalis in about 7 to 10
Thursday	days. At that time the caterpillars will
Friday	climb to the top of the container and hang
Week 2	down (head first) from the lid. The
Monday	chrysalis will take another 7 to 10 days
Tuesday	to develop into a butterfly.
Wednesday	
Thursday	
Friday	
Week 3	
Monday	
Tuesday	
Wednesday	
Thursday	
Friday	

❸ Predict what will happen next.

Answers will vary but the chrysalis should appear in 7 to 10 days. Students may predict that a butterfly will come out of the chrysalis.

Activity Book   Guided Inquiry **53**

---

❹ Draw pictures to show how the caterpillars changed.

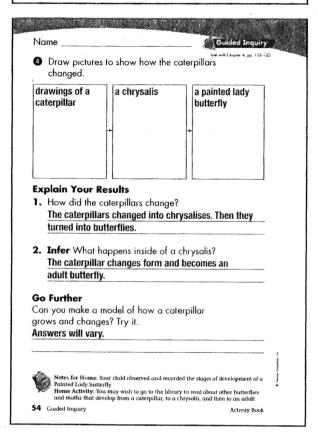

drawings of a caterpillar	a chrysalis	a painted lady butterfly

Explain Your Results

1. How did the caterpillars change?

The caterpillars changed into chrysalises. Then they turned into butterflies.

2. Infer What happens inside of a chrysalis?

The caterpillar changes form and becomes an adult butterfly.

Go Further

Can you make a model of how a caterpillar grows and changes? Try it.

Answers will vary.

Notes for Home: Your child observed and recorded the stages of development of a Painted Lady butterfly.
Home Activity: You may wish to go to the library to read about other butterflies and moths that develop from a caterpillar, to a chrysalis, and then to an adult.

54 Guided Inquiry   Activity Book

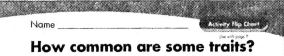
How common are some traits?

Fill in the chart below recording the number of students in your class with each trait.

Class Survey of Traits

Trait	Number of Students	Trait	Number of Students
Dimples		No dimples	
Free ear lobes		Attached earlobes	
Widow's peak		No widow's peak	

Explain Your Results

1. **Observe** Which trait do most of your classmates have?
   <u>Answers will vary.</u>

2. Which trait do the fewest of your classmates have?
   <u>Answers will vary.</u>

Notes for Home: Your child observed his/her classmates and collected data about the number of traits his/her classmates shared.
Home Activity: With your child, discuss the traits members of your family share.

What happens when a seed germinates?

In the chart below, draw what you **observe** each day for four days.

Day 1	Day 2	Day 3	Day 4

Explain Your Results

1. **Observe** How do you know if the seeds germinated?
   <u>The seed coat breaks open and a root starts growing.</u>

2. **Predict** In the box below, draw how you think the seeds would look after a week

   Drawings should show a longer root growing downward and a stem and leaves growing upward.

Notes for Home: Your child observed radish seeds germinate over a four-day period and predicted what the seeds would look like after a week.
Home Activity: With your child, plant seeds in a clear, plastic cup and observe the changes each day as the seeds germinate

Experiment Which bird beak can crush seeds?

Ask a question.
Which bird beak can crush seeds?

Make a hypothesis.
Answers will vary. Correct hypothesis: The cardinal has the kind of beak that can crush seeds.

Plan a fair test.
Be sure to use the same kind of clothespins for models of birds' beaks.

Do your test.
Follow steps 1 through 3

Collect and record data.

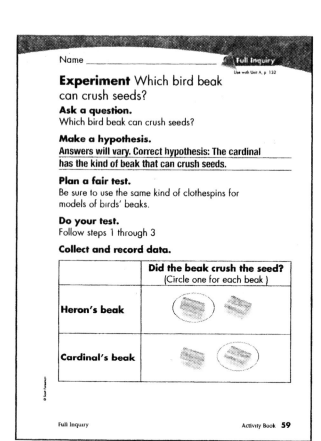

	Did the beak crush the seed? (Circle one for each beak)
Heron's beak	
Cardinal's beak	

Tell your conclusion.
Think about your test results Do you think a heron or a cardinal uses its beak to crush seeds?
A cardinal uses its beak to crush seeds.

Go Further
Which beak will pick up seeds faster? How can you find out?
Possible answer: The cardinal's beak will pick up seeds faster because it is hard to grab seeds with the heron's beak. I can find out by counting the number of seeds each beak can pick up in 1 minute.

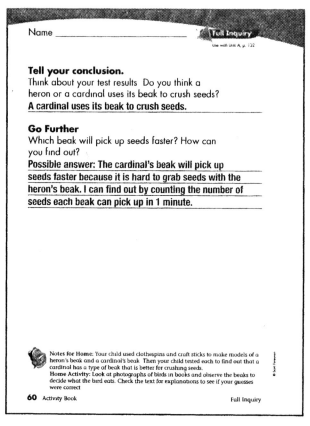

Notes for Home: Your child used clothespins and craft sticks to make models of a heron's beak and a cardinal's beak Then your child tested each to find out that a cardinal has a type of beak that is better for crushing seeds.
Home Activity: Look at photographs of birds in books and observe the beaks to decide what the bird eats. Check the text for explanations to see if your guesses were correct

Name _____ **Directed Inquiry**

Explore How are soils different?

Explain Your Results
Observe How are the soils alike?
Possible answer: Both of the soils are brown. They are
both made of little pieces.

How are they different?
Possible answer: The potting soil is softer and the
sandy soil is rougher. The potting soil smells stronger
than the sandy soil. The potting soil is darker than the
sandy soil, and it absorbs water faster.

Notes for Home: Your child compared the odor, appearance, grain size, texture,
and absorptive quality of potting soil and sandy soil.
Home Activity: Have your child examine soil in your backyard or in a park and
then describe it

Activity Book   Directed Inquiry **61**

Name _____ **Guided Inquiry**

Investigate How do worms change the soil?

❹ **Collect Data** Draw what happens inside
the bags.

Compost Bags		
	Bag With Worms	**Bag Without Worms**
Week 1	Drawing of a bag with soil, leaves, and worms. Show holes in the bag.	Drawing of a bag with soil and leaves.
Week 2	Drawing that shows fewer leaves on top.	Same drawing; no change
Week 3	Drawing that shows fewer leaves than Week 2.	Same drawing; no change

Activity Book   Guided Inquiry **63**

Name _____ **Guided Inquiry**

Explain Your Results

1. Which bag had more leaves after 3 weeks?
Probable answer: the bag without the worms.

2. Infer What did the worms do with the leaves?
The worms ate the leaves and mixed them into the soil.

Go Further
What would happen if you use more worms?
Investigate to find out:
More worms would make the leaves break down into
the soil faster.

Notes for Home: Your child learned how worms help in composting. He or she
learned that worms eat leaves and incorporate the waste matter into the soil
Home Activity: Have your child use what he or she learned to discuss this
question: *What happens to leaves in a forest? If no one rakes them up, where do the
leaves go?* (The leaves are composted, just as they were in this activity.)

64 Guided Inquiry   Activity Book

How does erosion affect land?

Record the data of the hill height below

Height of Hill Before Erosion	Estimated Height of Hill After Erosion	Height of Hill After Erosion
Answers may vary.	Answers may vary.	Answers may vary.

Explain Your Results

1. How did the height of the hill change after you sprinkled water on it?
The height of the hill decreased after water fell on it.

2. Infer How does rain affect the land?
Rain washes away the soil and
drops it someplace else.

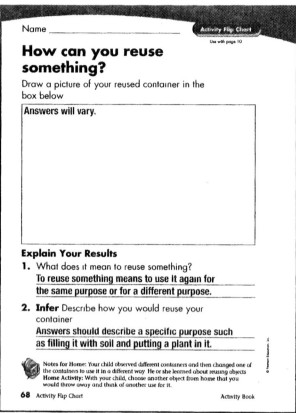

Notes for Home: Your child experimented with sand to see the effects that rain has on land. They observed that rain causes erosion on land
Home Activity: With your child, watch a rainstorm and observe erosion happening to the land

Activity Book   Activity Flip Chart **67**

How can you reuse something?

Draw a picture of your reused container in the box below

Answers will vary.

Explain Your Results

1. What does it mean to reuse something?
To reuse something means to use it again for
the same purpose or for a different purpose.

2. Infer Describe how you would reuse your container
Answers should describe a specific purpose such
as filling it with soil and putting a plant in it.

Notes for Home: Your child observed different containers and then changed one of the containers to use it in a different way. He or she learned about reusing objects
Home Activity: With your child, choose another object from home that you would throw away and think of another use for it.

68 Activity Flip Chart   Activity Book

© Pearson Education, Inc

Explore How much rain falls?

Explain Your Results

Infer How could you use this tool to measure how much rain falls?

Possible Answer: I could collect rain water in the jar and read the measurement on the jar.

Notes for Home: Your child made a rain gauge from a plastic jar and then used the tool to measure the amount of rainfall
Home Activity: Make a rain gauge at home. Use plastic food containers with a full-width mouth. Mark centimeters on masking tape along the side of the container

Activity Book   Directed Inquiry **69**

Investigate How can you measure weather changes?

❸ **Collect Data** Write how much rain fell each day. Write the temperature for each day

Rain and Temperature for One Week		
Day of the Week	rain gauge (centimeters)	thermometer (°C)
Monday		
Tuesday		
Wednesday		
Thursday		
Friday		

Activity Book   Guided Inquiry **71**

Explain Your Results

1. What does your chart tell you about the weather for one week?
Classify each day as rainy or not rainy.
Monday **Answers will vary.** _____
Tuesday _____
Wednesday _____
Thursday _____
Friday _____

2. Tell how the weather changed from day to day.
Answers will vary. _____
_____
_____

Go Further

How much rain do you think might fall in the next 5 days? Measure to find out.
Answers will vary. _____
_____
_____

Notes for Home: Your child used a rain gauge and a thermometer to measure rainfall and temperature for one week and recorded this information on a chart. Then your child explained what the data on the chart told him or her about the weather for the week
Home Activity: Follow the daily weather reports on the news and record the temperature or rainfall on a calendar for a few weeks or a month. Talk with your child about the weather based on the data you collected

72 Guided Inquiry   Activity Book

What happens when cold air meets warm air?

Record your observations of each jar below

Jar with warm water and red food coloring	Jar with cold water and blue food coloring
Jar had no to little condensation.	Jar had condensation on outside of it.

Explain Your Results

1. **Observe** What do you notice about the outside of the jars?

   Condensation or water droplets formed on the outside of the jar with blue (cold) water. The jar with the red (warm) water did not change or had only a small amount of condensation.

2. **Interpreting Data** Why do you think this happened?

   Water vapor in the warm air condensed onto the outside of the cold glass jar. The temperature difference was not as great with the warm jar so little or no water condensed there.

Notes for Home: Your child observed the process of condensation by observing a jar of warm water and a jar of cold water after ten minutes in sunlight
Home Activity: With your child, observe grass in the morning when there is dew and explain that this is also condensation.

Activity Book   Activity Flip Chart **75**

How can you tell that water is moving?

Draw a picture of what you observed in the box below.

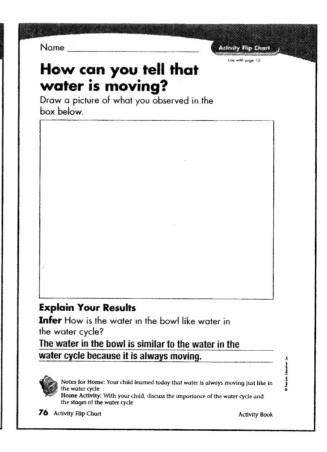

Explain Your Results

Infer How is the water in the bowl like water in the water cycle?

The water in the bowl is similar to the water in the water cycle because it is always moving.

Notes for Home: Your child learned today that water is always moving just like in the water cycle
Home Activity: With your child, discuss the importance of the water cycle and the stages of the water cycle

76 Activity Flip Chart   Activity Book

Explore Which fossils match the
plants and animals?

Explain Your Results
Communicate How did you match fossils to
plants and animals?
Possible answer: I knew this fossil went with this
animal because the shape of the teeth is the same.

Investigate How can you make
a model of a fossil?

❷ Tell about your fossil model and the shell.

How the Fossil Model and the Shell Are Alike and Different?	
How are they alike?	**How are they different?**
The marks on both are the same.	The model doesn't have colors.
The shape is the same.	You can only see one side of the model. The model is flatter.
	The shell is colored.

❹ **Observe** your partner's fossil model.
Guess what it is.
Answers will vary.

Explain Your Results
1. How did you **infer** what your partner's
fossil model was?
Possible answer: I used the size and shape of the
model fossil.

2. How do fossils give clues about living
things?
The shape, size, and marks on the fossils are the
same as parts of the real things. The fossils help you
picture what the real thing looked like.

Go Further
What else could you do to make models of
fossils? Make a plan and try it.
Answers will vary.

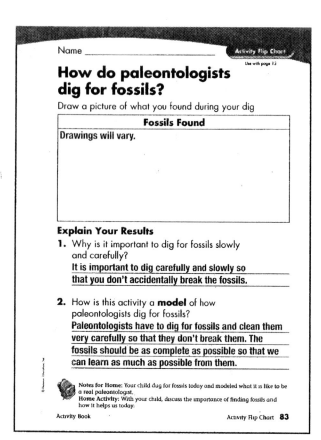

How do paleontologists dig for fossils?

Draw a picture of what you found during your dig

Fossils Found
Drawings will vary.

Explain Your Results

1. Why is it important to dig for fossils slowly and carefully?
   It is important to dig carefully and slowly so that you don't accidentally break the fossils.

2. How is this activity a **model** of how paleontologists dig for fossils?
   Paleontologists have to dig for fossils and clean them very carefully so that they don't break them. The fossils should be as complete as possible so that we can learn as much as possible from them.

Notes for Home: Your child dug for fossils today and modeled what it is like to be a real paleontologist.
Home Activity: With your child, discuss the importance of finding fossils and how it helps us today.

Activity Book   Activity Flip Chart **83**

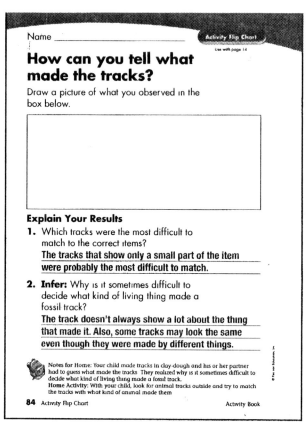

How can you tell what made the tracks?

Draw a picture of what you observed in the box below.

Explain Your Results

1. Which tracks were the most difficult to match to the correct items?
   The tracks that show only a small part of the item were probably the most difficult to match.

2. **Infer:** Why is it sometimes difficult to decide what kind of living thing made a fossil track?
   The track doesn't always show a lot about the thing that made it. Also, some tracks may look the same even though they were made by different things.

Notes for Home: Your child made tracks in clay-dough and his or her partner had to guess what made the tracks. They realized why is it sometimes difficult to decide what kind of living thing made a fossil track.
Home Activity: With your child, look for animal tracks outside and try to match the tracks with what kind of animal made them

84 Activity Flip Chart   Activity Book

Experiment Does gravel, sand, or soil make the best imprint?

Ask a question.
Which will make the best imprint?

Make your hypothesis.
Sample answer: I think the sand will make the best imprint.

Plan a fair test.
Use the same amount of sand, gravel, and potting soil on each plate.

Do your test.
Follow steps 1 through 3.

Collect and record data.
Fill in the chart. Use an **x** to show your results.

Which is the best imprint?			
	Best Imprint	**Some Imprint**	**No Imprint**
Gravel			X
Sand	X		
Soil		X	

Tell your conclusion.
Does gravel, sand, or soil make the best imprint?
Which would make the best imprint fossil?
Sand makes the clearest imprint. Soil would make the best imprint fossil.

Go Further
What might happen if you use wet gravel, sand, and soil? Try it and find out.
Possible answer: Wet soil will make a good imprint. Wet sand will make an imprint that will hold its shape.

Notes for Home: Your child made impressions of a shell in sand, potting soil, and gravel to understand how fossils are formed.
Home Activity: Make impressions of small objects in the soil around your home or at a park or at the beach.

Explore What happens when oil is mixed with water?

Explain Your Results

1. What happened when you mixed the oil and the water?
The oil and water did not blend together.
_____

2. Infer How could you separate oil from water?
Possible answer: You could use a spoon to scoop it from the top of the water.

Notes for Home: Your child combined oil and water and learned that these two liquids do not stay mixed
Home Activity: Mix salad oil and vinegar and shake to mix. Observe the results. Ask your child to compare this mixture with the mixture of oil and water made at school

---

Investigate How can water change?

❶ Describe the liquid water.
Possible answer: It is clear and flows.

What is the temperature of the liquid water?
10°C to 22°C

❷ Describe the frozen water.
Possible answer: It is cloudy (or clear), solid, and cold.

What is the temperature of the water after being in the freezer?
-109°C to 0°C

❸–❹ Predict What will happen to the water in a few hours? Will the temperature go up or down? What will happen to the outside of the cup?
Possible answers: The ice will melt. The temperature will go down as the ice melts. Drops of water will appear on the outside of the cup.

Record the temperatures on this chart.

How does the temperature change?	
Time	**Temperature °C**
After 30 minutes	Answers will vary.
After 1 hour	
After 2 hours	
After 3 hours	

Explain Your Results

1. Compare solid water to liquid water.
Solid water is hard and cold. Liquid water is clear, flows, and is warmer than ice.

2. Predict How long will it take for the liquid water to evaporate?
Possible answer: It may take a week or more for the water to evaporate entirely.

Go Further What other types of matter change when they are frozen? Investigate to find out
Possible answers: fruit, vegetables, soil

Notes for Home: Your child observed how the temperature and appearance of water changes as it freezes and thaws.
Home Activity: Observe how another liquid such as fruit juice changes when it is frozen Then predict and note how long it takes to thaw

How are solids different from liquids?

Classify the items by whether they are solid or liquid. List them in the correct category.

Solids	Liquids
stapler, fruit, block, gelatin, index cards	milk, juice, water

Explain Your Results

1. **Classify** How are the solids on your list alike? How are the liquids on your list alike?
   The solids are hard and have a shape. They do not need to be in a container. The liquids are wet and take the shape of the container they are in. You can pour a liquid; you can pick up a solid.

2. What other home or school items could you add to each list?
   Answers will vary, but could include any solids (eraser, chair, chalk) or liquids (soda, syrup, soup broth)

Notes for Home: Your child observed different materials and classified them by whether they were solid or liquid. They discussed how solids are similar and how liquids are similar.
Home Activity: With your child, find objects around the home that are solids and liquids. Do the solids have the same properties? Do the liquids have the same properties?

Activity Book   Activity Flip Chart **93**

How can you make an ice cube melt faster?

Record the time it took your ice cube to melt in the chart below.

Time It Took Ice Cube to Melt
Answers will vary.

Explain Your Results

1. **Communicate** Tell, write, or draw what you did to make your ice cube melt fast.
   Answers will vary. Students might describe the ice cube being heated or broken into smaller pieces.

2. **Predict** How could you melt an ice cube even faster?
   Answers will vary. Sample answer: Put the ice cube in a pan on the stove.

Notes for Home: Your child experimented with how to make an ice cube melt fast. He or she measured the time it took to melt an ice cube and predicted how it could melt even faster.
Home Activity: With your child, discuss what inventions have been made to help speed up the process of heating.

94 Activity Flip Chart   Activity Book

Name _____

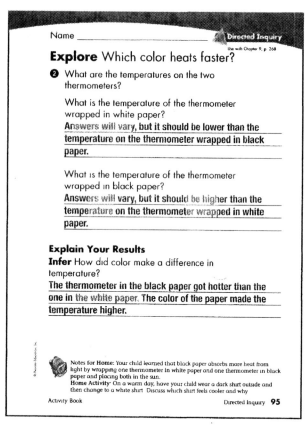

Directed Inquiry

Use with Chapter 9, p. 268

Explore Which color heats faster?

❷ What are the temperatures on the two thermometers?

What is the temperature of the thermometer wrapped in white paper?

Answers will vary, but it should be lower than the temperature on the thermometer wrapped in black paper.

What is the temperature of the thermometer wrapped in black paper?

Answers will vary, but it should be higher than the temperature on the thermometer wrapped in white paper.

Explain Your Results

Infer How did color make a difference in temperature?

The thermometer in the black paper got hotter than the one in the white paper. The color of the paper made the temperature higher.

Notes for Home: Your child learned that black paper absorbs more heat from light by wrapping one thermometer in white paper and one thermometer in black paper and placing both in the sun.
Home Activity: On a warm day, have your child wear a dark shirt outside and then change to a white shirt. Discuss which shirt feels cooler and why.

Activity Book   Directed Inquiry **95**

Name _____

Guided Inquiry

Use with Chapter 9, pp 290-291

Investigate How can you change light?

❸ **Observe** Draw what you see.

Changing Light

Activity Book   Guided Inquiry **97**

Name _____

Guided Inquiry

Use with Chapter 9, pp 290-291

Explain Your Results

1. What are some of the colors you saw?

Answer may include any or all of the following colors: red, orange, yellow, blue, green, purple

2. Infer How does light change when it passes through water?

The white light bends, and different colors can be observed.

Go Further How would using colored paper change the colors you see? Try it and find out.

Possible answer: All the colors will not show up on colored paper.

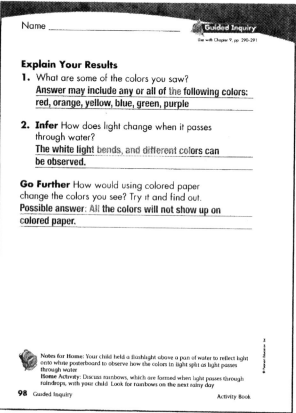

Notes for Home: Your child held a flashlight above a pan of water to reflect light onto white posterboard to observe how the colors in light split as light passes through water.
Home Activity: Discuss rainbows, which are formed when light passes through raindrops, with your child. Look for rainbows on the next rainy day.

98 Guided Inquiry   Activity Book

How does electricity make a light bulb light up?

In the box below, draw a picture of the closed circuit you made. Label the wires, battery, and light bulb

[box]

Explain Your Results

1. **Infer** What happens if only one wire touches the light bulb?
   The light bulb would not light up because the circuit would not be closed.

2. **Make and Use Models** What things do you need to make a closed circuit in this activity?
   You need wire, a battery, and a light bulb to make a closed circuit.

Notes for Home: Your child made a closed circuit using a battery, wire, and a light bulb
Home Activity: With your child, discuss where you could find closed circuits in your house

---

What gives off heat?

Record the temperatures you collected in the chart below

Location	Temperature
Desk top	Answers will vary.
Lamp	Answers will vary.
Sunlight	Answers will vary.
Your hand	Answers will vary.

Explain Your Results

1. **Infer** What things give off heat, according to the results of this activity?
   A lamp, the Sun, and the human body give off heat.

2. When you take the thermometer away from heat, the temperature of the thermometer goes down. What happens to the heat?
   It flows away from the thermometer.

Notes for Home: Your child used a thermometer to measure the temperature of different things that give off heat
Home Activity: With your child, use a thermometer to measure the temperature of various items to determine if they give off heat

Explore How can you measure force?

❶ How long is the rubber band when you pull it?
Answers will vary, **but the length should be approximately 25 cm.**

❷ Add 1 more book and pull. How long is the rubber band?
Answers will vary, **but the length should be approximately 40 cm.**

Explain Your Results
Communicate How are the measurements different?
The measurement with two books was higher. It took more force to move two books.

Notes for Home: Your child pulled one book, and then two books, with a rubber band and observed that the rubber band stretched more. Your child used a rubber band to measure force.
Home Activity: Use a small narrow rubber band to pull small light objects and heavy objects. Observe that the rubber band stretches more as it moves heavier objects.

Investigate What can magnets do?

❶ **Interpret Data** What happens when the N and S ends of the magnets are pushed together? What happens when the N and N ends of the magnets are pushed together?
The magnets stick together. The magnets push away (repel) each other.

❷ **Predict** which objects a magnet will pull
Try to pull each object
Answers will vary; correct predictions are steel or iron objects such as a safety pin, coin, paperclip.

❸ Can a magnet pull through the things listed in the chart? Record what you **observe**.

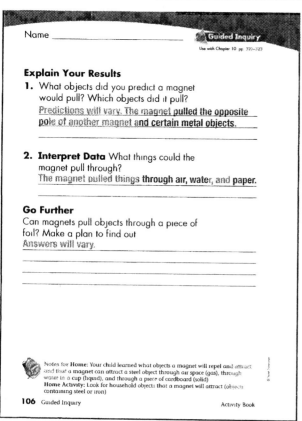

Can a magnet pull through these things?			
Air	Plastic Cup	Water	Paper
gas	solid	liquid	solid
yes	X		X	X
no		X		

Explain Your Results
1. What objects did you predict a magnet would pull? Which objects did it pull?
Predictions will vary. The magnet pulled the opposite pole of another magnet and certain metal objects.

2. Interpret Data What things could the magnet pull through?
The magnet pulled things **through air, water, and paper.**

Go Further
Can magnets pull objects through a piece of foil? Make a plan to find out
Answers will vary.

Notes for Home: Your child learned what objects a magnet will repel and attract and that a magnet can attract a steel object through air space (gas), through water in a cup (liquid), and through a piece of cardboard (solid)
Home Activity: Look for household objects that a magnet will attract (objects containing steel or iron)

© Pearson Education, Inc.

Do heavy objects fall faster than light objects?

Write your prediction and actual outcome of which object will fall faster below in the chart.

Prediction	Actual Outcome
Answers will vary.	Answers will vary.

Explain Your Results

1. Was your prediction correct? If not, how was your observation different than your prediction?
   Most students will probably predict that the heavy object will fall faster than the light object. However, they should observe that both objects fall at the same time.

2. **Make Definitions** What can you say about how heavy and light objects fall?
   Heavy and light objects fall at the same time.

Notes for Home: Your child experimented with two classroom objects to see which would fall faster. Your child made a prediction and then tested it to find out how light and heavy objects fall.
Home Activity: With your child, make a prediction about other objects around the house to see which would fall faster. Test your predictions.

How do objects move on different surfaces?

Record how far the washer moved on each surface in the chart below.

Table	Wood	Sandpaper
Answers will vary.	Answers will vary.	Answers will vary.

Explain Your Results

1. On which surface did the washer move the farthest?
   on the table top

2. **Interpret Data** Why did the washer move different amounts on different surfaces?
   Some surfaces cause more friction than others.

Notes for Home: Your child learned how friction causes objects to slow down their movement by measuring the distance a washer moved on a table, wood, and sand paper.
Home Activity: With your child, discuss how friction also causes heat. Rub your hands together to create friction and feel the warmth on your hands.

Explore How can you make sound?

❶ Push down on one end of the ruler. Let go.
   Observe. What do you hear?
   The ruler makes a sound.

❷ Slide the ruler back farther on the table.
   Push down on the ruler again. What do you hear?
   The ruler makes a different sound.

Explain Your Results
Observe Think about what you heard. How did the sound change when you moved the ruler back?
The sound was higher when I moved the ruler back.

Notes for Home: Your child placed a ruler on a table and pushed the free end to cause it to vibrate. Your child learned that vibration causes sounds
Home Activity: Observe the sounds caused by vibration around your home, such as the hum of the refrigerator

---

Investigate How can you change sound?

❸ Fill in the chart.

	Is the sound loud or soft?
Hard plucks	loud
Gentle plucks	soft

Infer What changes the sound?
The way you pluck the rubber bands.

❹ Move the pencils apart. **Predict** whether the sound will be higher or lower
Answers will vary.

---

❺ Fill in the chart.

	Is the sound high or low?
Pencils close	high
Pencils far apart	low

Explain Your Results
1. What made the sound high? What made the sound loud?
Moving the two pencils closer together made the sound high. Plucking hard made the sound loud.

2. Infer How could you make a quiet, low sound?
Possible answer: I can make a quiet, low sound by moving the pencils farther apart and plucking the rubber band gently.

Go Further
What other things can you do to change the sound? Investigate to find out
Answers will vary.

Notes for Home: Your child learned how to change volume and pitch of sound by playing a musical instrument made by stretching rubber bands around a cardboard box
Home Activity: Use large and small plastic food containers to make musical instruments. Use containers with lids as drums or fill containers with seeds or dried beans to make instruments to shake

---

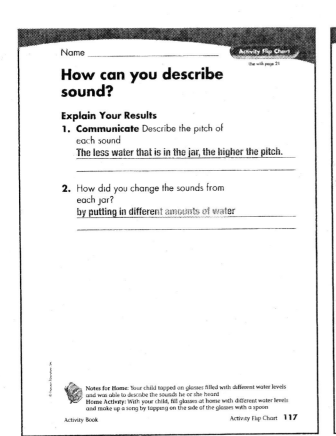

Name _____

How can you describe sound?

Explain Your Results

1. **Communicate** Describe the pitch of each sound

   The less water that is in the jar, the higher the pitch.

2. How did you change the sounds from each jar?

   by putting in different amounts of water

Notes for Home: Your child tapped on glasses filled with different water levels and was able to describe the sounds he or she heard
Home Activity: With your child, fill glasses at home with different water levels and make up a song by tapping on the side of the glasses with a spoon

Activity Book   Activity Flip Chart **117**

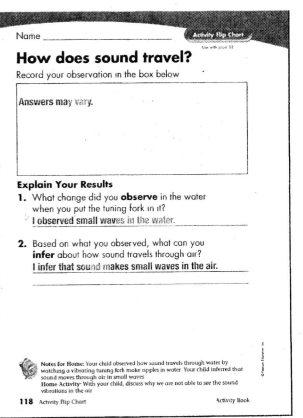

Name _____

How does sound travel?

Record your observation in the box below

Answers may vary.

Explain Your Results

1. What change did you **observe** in the water when you put the tuning fork in it?

   I observed small waves in the water.

2. Based on what you observed, what can you **infer** about how sound travels through air?

   I infer that sound makes small waves in the air.

Notes for Home: Your child observed how sound travels through water by watching a vibrating tuning fork make ripples in water Your child inferred that sound moves through air in small waves
Home Activity: With your child, discuss why we are not able to see the sound vibrations in the air

118 Activity Flip Chart   Activity Book

Experiment What kinds of objects reflect light clearly?

Ask a question.
What kinds of objects reflect light clearly?

Make your hypothesis.
Do smooth and shiny objects reflect light clearly? Tell what you think.
Shiny and smooth objects will reflect light.

Plan a fair test.
Make sure the objects are the same size. Use the same flashlight.

Do your test.
Write your **observations** in the chart on the next page.
❶ Is the mirror smooth? Is it shiny?
❷ Does the mirror reflect light clearly?
❸ Test the other objects. Do steps 1 and 2 again.

Collect and record your data.

	Is it smooth? yes or no	Is it shiny? yes or no	Does it reflect light clearly? yes or no
mirror	yes	yes	yes
paper	yes	no	no
wrinkled foil	no	yes	no
wrinkled paper	no	no	no

Tell your conclusion.
Do smooth and shiny objects reflect light clearly? How do you know?
Yes, because smooth, shiny objects made a bright reflection.

Go Further
What might happen if you test other classroom objects? Experiment to find out.
Possible answer: Other shiny objects will reflect light, but rough, dull objects will not.

 Notes for Home: Your child used a flashlight to shine light on objects to find out which objects will reflect light onto a wall
Home Activity: Place smooth and shiny household objects next to a light colored wall. Shine a flashlight on them to see if the object will reflect light onto the wall

Name _____

Use with Chapter 12, p. 384

Explore What causes day and night?

Explain Your Results

How does your **model** show day and night?

The flashlight is like the Sun. The ball is like Earth.

I can turn the ball to show how the Sun shines on Earth.

When one side of Earth turns away from the Sun it is night.

When a side of Earth is facing the Sun, it is day on that

side.

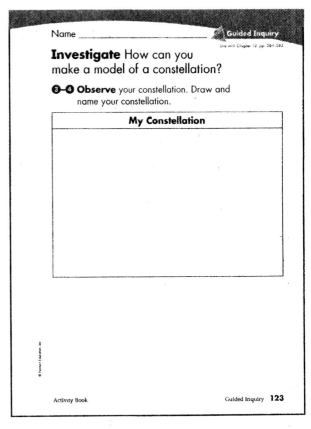

Notes for Home: Your child observed models to understand that when the Sun lights the side of Earth we are living on, it is daytime; and when that part of Earth turns away from the Sun it is nighttime.
Home Activity: Observe the Sun in the sky in the morning and evening of one day. Discuss how the Sun's position changed because Earth has moved.

Activity Book   Directed Inquiry **121**

Name _____

Use with Chapter 12, pp. 384-385

Investigate How can you make a model of a constellation?

③–④ Observe your constellation. Draw and name your constellation.

My Constellation

Notes for Home: Your child learned to identify and make a constellation by shining a light through holes in paper.
Home Activity: Look for constellations in the night sky. In the winter, look for three stars in a row that make up Orion's belt. Look for the Big Dipper (seven stars that form the shape of a ladle).

Activity Book   Guided Inquiry **123**

Name _____

Use with Chapter 12, pp. 384-385

Explain Your Results

1. Tell about your constellation. How is your model like a real constellation?
   Answers will vary.

   How is it different from a real constellation?
   Answers will vary.

2. **Make a definition** of a constellation.
   Answers will vary, but should include the idea that
   groupings of stars make patterns in the sky.

Go Further

How else could you make a model of your constellation? Investigate to find out.
Answers will vary.

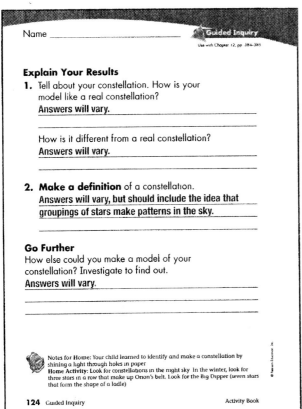

124 Guided Inquiry   Activity Book

What causes the seasons?

Explain Your Results

1. Infer Each position stands for Earth at the beginning of a different season. Which position is the beginning of winter where you live? Which position is the beginning of summer?

<u>winter—A; summer—C</u>

2. What causes the seasons to change where you live?

<u>Earth's tilt and its movement in its orbit around the</u>
<u>Sun cause the seasons to change in any one place.</u>

Notes for Home: Your child learned about Earth's rotation around the Sun and what causes the different seasons. He/she learned about the Sun's position on Earth when it is the beginning of the summer and winter seasons where we live.
Home Activity: With your child, watch the Sun as it rises and sets. Note the direction the Sun rises and sets each day.

What do constellations look like?

Explain Your Results

Communicate Suppose you connect the dots differently. What other animal or object might the constellation look like?

<u>Answers will vary. For example, for students who</u>
<u>chose the Big Dipper, they might imagine that the</u>
<u>handle of the Big Dipper is an animal's tail (Actually, it is.</u>
<u>The Big Dipper is part of the Big Bear constellation with</u>
<u>the handle forming the bear's tail.)</u>

Notes for Home: Your child made up his/her own constellation, made a model of it using glow in the dark dot stickers, and gave it a name.
Home Activity: With your child, go outside at nighttime and look for a constellation in the sky.

Explore How can you move the ball?

Explain Your Results

Communicate Tell how you solved the problem
Students may give any of the following solutions.
a. We used the magnet to pick up the ball and move it to the cup. We knocked the ball from the magnet by shaking it (or hitting it against the side of the cup).
b. We used the pencil (or ruler) to push the ball onto the spoon. We used the spoon to carry the ball to the cup.
c. We used the spoon (or pencil or ruler) to push the cup over to the stack of books. We used the spoon (or pencil or ruler) to push the ball off the stack of books into the cup.
d. We used the ruler as a ramp. We put one end of the ruler between the cover and the pages of the book at the top. We put the other end of the ruler over the edge of the cup. Then we used the pencil (or spoon) to push the ball on the groove in the ruler. The ball rolled down the ruler ramp into the cup.

Notes for Home: Your child solved the problem of getting a metal ball in a cup using a magnet, ruler, pencil, and spoon
Home Activity: Encourage your child to think up solutions to everyday problems such as how to clean up his or her room (for example, use a cup to pull objects across the floor or use posterboard as a chute to place puzzle pieces into a box)

Investigate How can you make a maze?

❶ How can you make a maze that a marble can follow? Draw your plan here.

❸ **Predict** Will your maze work? _____

❹ Test your maze. Then move the tubes to make the maze work better

---

❺ Test your maze two more times.

Test your maze.	
Test	**Did the marble follow the maze?**
1	
2	
3	

Explain Your Results

Communicate Tell how the parts of your maze work together.
Answers will vary. _____
_____
_____

Go Further
How can you make your marble move in a different way? Investigate to find out.
Answers will vary. _____
_____

Notes for Home: Your child used paper tubes in different ways to make a variety of mazes Your child used trial and error to retape the tubes in a pattern to successfully get a marble through the paper-tube maze
Home Activity: Have your child recreate his or her maze at home using masking tape to attach paper tubes to cardboard

Name _____

How can you make a model of a helicopter?

Draw a picture of your two model helicopters in the box below.

Answers will vary.

Explain Your Results

1. **Observing** How are your two models different?
   Answers will vary. Models may differ in length, width, and shape of rotors.

2. How do the models fly differently? Why do you think they do?
   Answers will vary. Models may fly differently by falling farther before they start spinning, by falling more slowly, or by moving farther away before hitting the floor. Students should focus on at least one different aspect of design for why the flights are different.

Notes for Home: Your child made two models of helicopters and compared how they flew differently because of the way that they were made
Home Activity With your child, make models of helicopters and a target. Try to get your model helicopters to land on the target Which model worked the best and why?

Activity Book

Activity Flip Chart **135**

How can you build a strong bridge?

Record your prediction and actual outcome of how much weight your bridge will hold in the chart below.

Prediction: How Much Weight?	Actual Outcome: How Much Weight?
Answers will vary.	Answers will vary.

Explain Your Results

1. What shapes are in your bridge?
   Most bridges will probably have triangles, squares, and rectangles.

2. **Interpret Data:** Do you think the shape of a bridge affects how strong it is? Why do you say that?
   Yes, because different bridges of different designs held different amounts of weight.

Notes for Home: Your child built a model of a bridge and made a prediction of how much weight it would hold Then your child tested his or her bridge and recorded how much weight it could hold Your child learned that the shape of a bridge affects how strong it is.
Home Activity: With your child, make a bridge out of clay and out of craft sticks. Test the bridge to find out how much weight it can hold

136 Activity Flip Chart

Activity Book

Experiment Which tissue is the strongest?

Ask a question.
Are tissues that cost more stronger than tissues that cost less?

Make your hypothesis.
Possible answer: If a tissue costs the most, then it is the strongest.

Plan a fair test.
Use the same amount of water to wet each tissue. Use 3 different brands of tissue. Each should have a different cost.

Do your test.
Follow steps 1 through 6.

Collect and record data.
Show how many marbles it takes to break the tissue and how much the marbles weigh Record your data on page 138

The strength of 3 different types of tissues may vary and the number and mass of marbles needed to tear each of the tissues will probably be different. Measurements will not be exact.

Tissue Cost	How many marbles?	How many grams?
Most	19	98
Middle	17	86
Least	7	36

Sample answers

Tell your conclusion.
Which tissue is the strongest?
Sample answer: The brand that costs the most is the strongest tissue. It took 15 marbles to tear it. It is the strongest because it is the thickest one.

Go Further
What if you used less water to wet each tissue? Try it and find out.
Possible answer: If you don't use as much water, the tissues can hold more marbles.

Notes for Home: You child tested how many marbles a wet tissue can support to find out which of three tissues is the strongest
Home Activity: Try this experiment at home Stretch three types of tissue over jars with rubber bands. Wet the tissue and place a number of small heavy objects (such as rocks) on each tissue until it breaks.